SIR ISAAC NEWTON

SIR ISAAC NEWTON

This portrait is from MacArdel's mezzotint after E. Seeman's painting, one of the most refined and interesting extant. It was painted in 1726 and presented by Thomas Hollis to Trinity College in 1761. The half-tone plate is lent through the courtesy of Dr. David Eugene Smith and Ginn and Company.

SIR ISAAC NEWTON
1727 - 1927

A Bicentenary Evaluation of His Work

A SERIES OF PAPERS
PREPARED UNDER THE AUSPICES OF

THE HISTORY OF SCIENCE SOCIETY

IN COLLABORATION WITH

*The American Astronomical Society, The American
Mathematical Society, The American Physical
Society, The Mathematical Association
of America and Various Other
Organizations*

BALTIMORE
THE WILLIAMS & WILKINS COMPANY
1928

SPECIAL PUBLICATION No. 1
OF THE
HISTORY OF SCIENCE SOCIETY

COMPOSED AND PRINTED AT THE
WAVERLY PRESS
FOR
THE WILLIAMS & WILKINS COMPANY
BALTIMORE, MD., U. S. A.

CONTENTS

[v]

INTRODUCTION

IT IS a gratifying proof of the existence of a Commonwealth of Science that the two-hundredth anniversary of Newton's death has seen, in so many parts of the world, gatherings of scholars to recognize his achievements and to honor his memory. That such a gathering should have taken place in the English-speaking countries of the Americas was therefore natural, not so much because of any linguistic force of gravity, but because of the natural brotherhood of those who work in the fields of Newton's many interests.

The papers here published were purposely limited as to length and style. It was the intention of the Society to encourage the preparation of articles which would not merely describe the fields of Newton's activities, but would do so in language that appeals to educated readers in general rather than merely to a small number of highly trained scholars. With this purpose in view the several authors set about to popularize their records of his contributions to scholarship, but without vulgarizing them. That they succeeded in this attempt is evident from the articles themselves. These cover a wide range of human activity, and in so doing they represent the great diversity of Newton's interests—a diversity that was more possible two centuries ago than would be the case, even to a mind like his, at the present time.

To most students Newton is known for some single line of achievement. It is, therefore, a privilege to have set before us an intellectual symposium which allows us to form a broader idea of his remarkable gifts. That such a master as Professor Miller in the field of optics should tell us of Newton's work in this subject; that Professor Birkhoff should so clearly compare the essential features of Einstein's theory with the theory of gravitation and show us that one is the complement rather than the destroyer of the other; and that President Campbell should reveal to us the vision of Newton in the theory of astrophysics, a subject that we look upon as purely modern—all this is not merely stimulating, it is invigorating to our intellectual life. The same is equally true of the paper by Dr. Heyl, who shows us the experimental bent of mind of the mathematician, and of Professor Brown's practical survey of the influence of Newton's work. Professor Cajori has given us the benefit of his extensive studies into the cause of delay in announcing the Law of Gravitation, and into the nature of the fluxional calculus which, a century after Newton's death, began to yield to the advance of the differential theory.

Three of the papers open what is, to most of us,

a new view of the activities of the mathematician in the domains of chemistry, religion, and finance. In the second of these fields we are apt to think of Newton as a mere theologian of the old school, whereas Professor Brett has shown that he was really one of the most influential predecessors of the modern religious thinkers. In his work at the mint we are commonly led to feel that he took a sinecure and neglected to use an intellect from which the world had a right to expect something worth while; but Mr. Roberts shows him in a light that, to most of us, is entirely new—that of a financier of foresight and one with a firm grasp of a large problem. And finally, Mr. Brasch has shown us that Newton's work came early to be appreciated in the American colonies, and that it received adequate treatment at the hands of one of our earliest scholars, John Winthrop.

It is with the belief that the publication of these papers will lead to a better comprehension of the the work of England's greatest scientist—an expression always to be understood with respect to the time in which a man lived—and to a more rational appreciation of his achievements, that the History of Science Society has arranged for the publication of this volume, and that the publishers have so generously undertaken the task.

DAVID EUGENE SMITH.

[ix]

NEWTON IN THE LIGHT OF
MODERN CRITICISM

NEWTON IN THE LIGHT OF MODERN CRITICISM

DAVID EUGENE SMITH, Ph.D., LL.D.

President of the History of Science Society, Professor Emeritus of Mathematics, Teachers College, Columbia University

OF THE esteem in which Newton's work has been held for two centuries there is no question. Few men have ever fared so well. The justness of that esteem has, however, been seriously questioned by various scholars of reputation. There have been assertions that his word was not "as good as his bond;" that his influence upon British mathematics was not salutary; that he abandoned the altar of science for the fleshpots of Egypt; that the foundations of his greatest mathematical theory were weak and the theory was unstable; and that he stands as a fetich for the unthinking worship of the Anglo-Saxon. Nor have there been lacking expressions to the effect that, had he been the great genius that England asserts, his countrymen would long since have given to the public a definitive edition of his complete works, his correspondence, and his papers. Such editions are a common tribute paid by nations or societies to the memory of their great men. Why should England have published

[3]

the monumental editions of Cayley's and Sylvester's works, and yet have so neglected Newton and have allowed the Portsmouth papers to lie practically in oblivion? Was there not, back of all the praise, a feeling that the nation had risen to his defense in an inglorious dispute, but that at heart it doubted his greatness?

These questions have not been raised merely by men of no intellectual capacity who seek a place in the limelight by decrying the work of others; by those, who, as a French philosopher has put it, rail at greatness because they cannot achieve it. They come from honest-minded men who really wish to know what it was that Newton accomplished to make him worthy of the acclaim that has been accorded him; who ask for an answer, without excess of praise, to the justifiable question, "What were Newton's real contributions to world knowledge?"

There is also the relatively subordinate but always interesting question of Newton the man. Carlyle was probably right in asserting that our race is largely composed of hero worshippers. Is our estimate of Newton an evidence of the truth of this assertion? We hear of him as a scholar, but what of him as a man?

Was he the hero when he closed the oak at Trinity to open the gate of fortune at the Mint?

[4]

One of his countrymen speaks of his being "translated to the temple of Mammon, at the time when the differential calculus was, in the hands of Leibniz and the Bernoullis, beginning to rise into higher stories." "Had Newton remained at his post," he adds, "coining nothing but ideas, the mathematical science might have gained a century of advance." Is this judgment just? Would scientific progress have been materially hastened had Newton stayed at Cambridge, or is it a sad fact that his genius for discovery had already burned itself out? Did Newton leave because he felt that his powers had failed him, or was it because he could not exist upon his stipend, or did he yearn for the pleasures of Leicester Square, or Jermyn Street, or Kensington? Which was right in his diagnosis, his biographer, Sir David Brewster, or that caustic but unbalanced critic, De Morgan? The former excuses his desertion by saying, "At the age of fifty, the high-priest of science found himself the inmate of a college, and, but for the generous patronage of a friend, he would have died within its walls." Upon which De Morgan bitingly comments, "and where should a high-priest of science have lived and died? At the Mint?"

Was he really the scholar devoted to the search for truth or, after all, was he simply, as some critic says, "very much the man of the world"

[5]

who "stuck to the main chance" and died wealthy?

Was he a man who, as De Morgan further says, gave uterance to what had "the clearest appearance of a direct and deliberate falsehood,"—"betrayed by the necessities of his case into that culpable evasion in which self-love finds excuse"? And if so, could he have at the same time have been, as his latest biographer has claimed, "a power in the intellectual field of human activity whose supremacy has been almost unchallenged for centuries, and bids fair to remain unchallenged for generations to come"?[1]

To me, the documents of two of his periods of life are particularly interesting. The first is his notebook of the Grantham and early Cambridge days, revealing his boyish interests in everything human—painting, conjuring, fishing, chemistry, colors, drugs, trigonometry, and the church calendar. It gives us new proof that "the child is father of the man," and it unveils such a wholesome picture of a wholesome boy who was just beginning to know the joy of living—of living the intellectual life and of revelling in its riches! Of documents of the second period, one is his signature to a memorandum relating to the trial of a counterfeiter, and seems to have been made the very week

[1] Professor S. Brodetsky, *Sir Isaac Newton*, London, 1927, p. 3.

in which he became Warden of the Mint. The other is a document written considerably later, acknowledging the receipt of certain taxes. These always seem so full of pathos. That Newton, of all men born upon British soil, should have passed his later years in looking after clippers of coin or in acting as a gatherer-in of taxes seems to me particularly pathetic, even though he was still a power in the Royal Society and a contributor to its proceedings.

In reality, if one is a slave to the old fallacy of *post hoc ergo propter hoc*, he has abundant reasons for feeling that Newton's genius was a blight upon mathematical activity in Great Britain for a dozen decades. In any case it was not stimulating. Before him there had been some of the giants upon whose shoulders he confessed to stand—men like Harriot, Oughtred, Napier, and Barrow. With him stood Wallis, Halley, Cotes, and De Moivre. After him his countrymen seemed content to rest upon the fame which he had brought them, and for Great Britain the eighteenth century was relatively a period of mathematical sterility; while in continental Europe great progress was being made at the instigation of men like the Bernoulli's, Euler, d'Alembert, Lambert, Lagrange, Laplace, Carnot, Legendre, Monge, Delambre, Lacroix, Mascheroni, Ruffini, Pfaff, and that rising genius, Gauss.

[7]

As to optics, Professor Brodetsky, one of his latest biographers,[2] and himself a scientist, has made the strong assertion—"The weight of Newton's authority delayed optical progress for many generations. It was not Newton's fault, of course; it was the fault of the lesser men who followed him and mistook idolatry for sincere admiration."

Shall we say that we too have joined in the worship of an idol in the Temple of Science, or shall we say that Newton was at the same time a genius and a man who was intensely human? We have positive evidence of an interesting kind in the boyish notebook already mentioned, and now in the Pierpont Morgan Library. This shows clearly that he had, when in school at Grantham, an abundance of the inquisitiveness of youth but that he gave no particular promise of a brilliant life. He learned more from the old apothecary in whose house he lodged than he did at school, and the learning was of a more human type. His early work at Trinity gave no more evidence of unusual success than that of thousands of others who travel by similar paths. He scattered his interests with the recklessness of youth even when he had come to middle life. He experienced what we apologetically speak of as "straightened circumstances, "as the great majority of men do at some time in their

[2] Professor S. Brodetsky, *Sir Isaac Newton*, London, 1927, p. 80.

[8]

lives. He loved the solitude of a student and yet abandoned it for a life in the social atmosphere of the metropolis. He challenged a royal decree and later accepted a knighthood. He dreaded controversy and yet, when forced to it, as shown in two notable instances, would valiantly assert his rights. Because he could not subscribe to church dogmas, he declined to take holy orders, and yet he wrote upon and reverenced religion. He needed the whip to make him publish his discoveries, content, like Pythagoras, with revealing them only to his own initiates. As already stated, his countryman, De Morgan, accuses him of conniving in deceit and there were contemporaries who were even more outspoken. He left Cambridge, where he had built himself a name, and went to London where he built himself a fortune. In advancing years he evidenced more and more a profound faith in a divine Being, just as most other men have tended to do. In other words, here was a very human being, with human virtues and human frailties, and yet a succession of pilgrims continually stand in silent awe before his monument in the Valhalla of the British World—and may we not unite in saying that they are justified in so doing?

We should like to know the cause of this human being's dread of publicity, of completing a given task, and of criticism from those who were recognized as scholars by others than themselves. Why, when he had discovered the theory of the sextant in 1700, did he rest content to let it remain unknown, save by a letter to Halley, and thus to allow Hadley to reinvent it and receive credit for it thirty years later, when Newton was already dead? Why did he allow his theory of gravitation to lie almost untouched for such a term of years? Why did he delay the announcement of the construction of the reflecting telescope until prodded by his friends to make it known to the Royal Society? And why did he allow his theory of fluxions to lie for nearly thirty years before it was really made public?

It was a feeling natural to most sensitive men that once led him to say, in view of petty criticisms by petty minds, "I see I have made myself a slave to philosophy. . . . . I will resolutely bid adieu to it eternally, excepting what I do for my private satisfaction, or I will leave it to come out after me; for I see that a man must either resolve to put out nothing new, or to become a slave to defend it."

When we review his life, his idiosyncracies, his periods of contrast, and his doubts and ambitions and desire for place, may we not take some pleasure in thinking of him as a man—a man like most other men save in one particular—he had genius—a greater touch of divinity than comes to the rest of us? Few men have ever lived who explored so successfully as wide a range of human activities and few who could so justly have used the well-known phrase, *Homo sum, et nihil humani a me alienum puto.*

NEWTON AND OPTICS

NEWTON AND OPTICS

DAYTON C. MILLER, D.Sc., LL.D.

Ambrose Swasey Professor of Physics, Case School of Applied Science

THE world is not now just discovering Newton's greatness; in his own lifetime he was regarded as the greatest man in intellectual achievement which the world had known; the highest possible posthumous honors were done him. Lagrange, referring to the *Principia* called it "the greatest production of the human mind," and Laplace said that it is assured for all time of "a preeminence above all other productions of the human intellect." Voltaire, a contemporary, said of Newton: "If all the geniuses of the universe were assembled, he should lead the band." The appreciation of his greatness has continued through the two centuries that have elapsed since his death. Newton's contributions to philosophy are so numerous and varied, and so profound, that they affect not only science and philosophy, but through them, they have affected our modern civilization as a whole.

Newton lived to be more than eighty-four years of age, retaining to the end his full intellectual powers. He spent his boyhood and school days on the small farm at Woolsthorpe and in the school

[15]

in the small village of Grantham. He entered
Trinity College, Cambridge, when he was nineteen
years old. In January, 1665, he took the degree of
Bachelor of Arts, being just over twenty-two
years of age. Both in 1665 and 1666 Trinity
College was dismissed on account of the plague,
and Newton spent the greater part of the time at
his home, and made many remarkable mathematical
studies, such as the discovery of the binominal
theorem, and the first theory of fluxious (the calculus). About this time he purchased prisms and
lenses, and chemicals and a melting furnace. He
returned to Cambridge, and in October, 1667, was
elected a Fellow of Trinity College; in the following
year he took the degree of Master of Arts. Dr.
Barrow had been the first Lucasian Professor of
Mathematics in the University, and when he
resigned in 1668, he nominated Newton, then
twenty-six years old, as his successor, and this was
confirmed. The duties of the professorship required Newton to give one lecture a week for one
term of each year, and to devote two hours per
week to audiences with students who wished to
consult with him about their work. Newton
chose to lecture on optics, but the lectures were not
formally published till thirty-five years later.

The sixty-two years of his life after graduation
was divided into two rather distinct and equal

portions; he spent thirty-one years, till he was fifty-three years of age, as a college graduate and fellow and professor at Cambridge University; and thirty-one more years in London in the midst of public affairs of the nation and as the doyen of British science. It is a conspicuous fact that nearly all of his great contributions to science were formulated within a period of about ten years immediately following his graduation, from 1665 to 1675, when he was from twenty-two to thirty-two years of age.

Before describing Newton's discoveries, the work of some of his predecessors will be mentioned.

Newton was born in the year in which Galileo died, and only twelve years after the death of Kepler. The Copernican Theory had been vindicated by Galileo's invention and application of the telescope; the movements of the earth and the planets had been correctly described. The new science of dynamics was correctly set forth by Galileo, and the true scientific method was widely recognized. The new astronomy, with its revolutionary interpretation of the solar system and the universe, was making a profound impression, and the newly invented telescope created an intense interest in optical problems. Improvements upon the Galilean form of telescope had been made by Kepler, who in his books on optics, sets forth the present-day type of refractor except for the achromatic objective. There were serious defects in the focal images of these instruments, which were then attributed solely to spherical abberation. Descartes published the correct theoretical treatment of this problem, and gave designs for lenses with elliptical or hyperbolic curvature which would be free from spherical abberation. Then there followed quickly great improvements by Hevelius, Huygens and others. Telescopes of focal length up to two hundred and ten feet were constructed. In 1664, fifty-three years after Galileo made the first telescope, James Gregory, a famous Scottish mathematician, published his work on Optics, in which he described the type of reflecting telescope, which now bears his name. At this time, Newton, aged twenty-one years, and in his second year at Cambridge, had already read Kepler's *Optics*, the works of Descartes, and other up-to-date mathematical books; and he had the advantage of studying under one of the foremost mathematicians, Dr. Barrow. Newton thus had the fullest knowledge of the scientific work of the day, and of the great scientific puzzels awaiting solution, among which were: "Why do the planets move as described by Copernicus and Kepler?" and "What is the nature of light?"

Newton's first scientific observations of importance seem to be those made in 1664, a year before his graduation, when he observed and measured lunar halos and "crowns"; his note-book of this year contains calculations about musical notes, geometrical propositions, the "Arithmetic of Infinites," the extraction of roots, together with observations on refraction, on the grinding of "spherical optic glasses," and on the errors of lenses.

In the year, 1668, Newton made the first reflecting telescope, but he had not yet discovered the nature of the spectrum, for in 1669 he helped Dr. Barrow in the publication of Barrow's lectures on *Optics*, in which an erroneous theory of color is set forth. In the autumn of 1671, he made a second reflecting telescope and the fame of his researches, especially in optics, began to spread. He was proposed as a candidate for admission to the Royal Society in December, 1671, and was asked to send the reflecting telescope to the Society for inspection. The instrument was exhibited before the Society in January, 1672, at which time a description of the telescope was read, and Newton was elected a Fellow of the Society. This telescope has ever since remained with the Society as one of its most cherished possessions. Newton was very much pleased with the honor of election to the Royal Society, and his acknowledgement, sent one week later, says:

"I desire that in your next letter you will inform me for what time the society continue their weekly meetings; because, if they continue them for any time, I am purposing them to be considered of and examined on account of a philosophical discovery, which induced me to the making of the said telescope, and which I doubt not but will prove much more grateful than the communication of that instrument, being in my judgment the oddest if not the most considerable detection which hath hitherto been made into the operations of nature."

This promise was fulfilled by a communication which was read just one month later, and the "considerable detection into the operations of nature" proved to be the explanation of the nature of the solar spectrum, and the true theory of color.

After Newton had discovered the spectrum, he made other important investigations of optical phenomena, which were concluded about the year 1676. Nothing more was done in the domain of optics until, in 1704, he published the first edition of his book called *Opticks; or a Treatise on the Reflections, Refractions, Inflections and Colours of Light*. There were slight additions made in the second edition which appeared in 1718. For our present purpose, it seems desirable to give a description of the contents of this book, which covers all of the work in optics. A number of excerpts are given, which are often interesting because of the forms of expression as well as for their content. To facilitate references, page numbers in parenthesis are given; these refer to *Opticks*, second edition, London, 1718.

The treatise on *Opticks* is an octavo volume of 382 pages; it is written in the English language, which was unusual at that time for a scientific work. It is divided into three books and the books are sub-divided into "parts." The original preface, called "Advertisement" states:

"Advertisement 1. Part of the ensuing Discourse about Light was written at the Desire of some Gentlemen of the Royal Society, in the year 1675, and then sent to their Meetings, and the rest was added about twelve years after to complete the Theory; except the Third Book and the last observation in the last Part of the Second, which were since put together out of scatter'd Papers. To avoid being engaged in Disputes about these matters, I have hitherto delayed the printing, (for twenty-nine years), and should still have delayed it, had not the Importunity of Friends prevailed upon me." (p. 1.)

The first book gives certain "Definitions" and "Axioms," and then treats of refraction and reflection in general, of the solar spectrum and of reflecting telescopes. The second book treats of the colors of thin plates, of the colors of natural bodies, and of the nature of light. The third book considers diffraction, double refraction in crystals, and general philosophical problems.

The first book begins with the sentence: "My design in this book is not to explain the Properties of Light by Hypotheses, but to propose and prove them by reason and experiments." The first fifteen pages are given to the consideration of eight axioms.

"I have now given in Axioms and their Explications the sum of what hath hitherto been treated of in Opticks. For what hath been generally agreed on I content myself to assume under the notion of Principles, in order to what I have farther to write. And this may suffice for an introduction to Readers of quick Wit and good Understanding not yet versed in Opticks: Although those who are already acquainted with this Science, and have handled glasses, will more readily apprehend what followeth." (p. 15.)

The experiment with the prism is thus described:

"In the Sun's Light let into my darkened Chamber through a small round hole in my Window-Shut, I placed a Lens. . . . Then immediately after the Lens I placed a Prism, . . . and thereby the round Image which the Lens alone did cast upon the Paper might be drawn out into a long one with parallel Sides. . . . Yet instead of the circular hole F 'tis better to substitute an oblong hole shaped like a long Parallelogram with its length parallel to the Prism. . . . The edges also of the Prism and Lens. . . . must be covered with a black Paper glewed on. And all the Light of the Sun's beam let into the Chamber which is useless and unprofitable to the Experiment, ought to be intercepted with black Paper. . . . In trying these things so much diligence is not altogether necessary, but it will promote the success of the Experiments, and by a very scrupulous Examiner of things deserves to be applied. It's difficult to get Glass Prisms fit for this purpose, and therefore I used sometimes prismatick Vessels made with pieces of broken Looking-glasses, and filled with Rain Water. And to increase the Refraction, I sometimes impregnated the Water strongly with Saccharum Saturni (Sugar of Lead)." (p. 57-62.)

"Homogeneal Light is refracted regularly without any Dilatation splitting or shattering of the Rays, and the confused Vision of Objects seen through refracting Bodies of heterogeneal Light arises from the different Refrangibility of several sorts of Rays." (p. 62.)

Newton's consideration of the defects of telescopes is of such interest that more extended quotations will be given.

"The Imperfection of Telescopes is vulgarly

[23]

attributed to the spherical Figures of the glasses, and therefore Mathematicians have propounded to figure them by the conical Sections. To shew that they are mistaken, I have inserted this Proposition. . . ." (p. 71.)

"Now by what has been said, it's certain that the Rays which differ in Refrangibility do not converge to the same focus, but if they flow from a lucid point, as far from the Lens on one side as their Foci are on the other, the Focus of the most refrangible Rays shall be nearer to the Lens than that of the least refrangible, by above the fourteenth part of the whole distance; and if they flow from a lucid point, so very remote from the Lens that before their Incidence they may be accounted parallel, the Focus of the most refrangible Rays shall be nearer to the Lens than the Focus of the least refrangible, by about the 27th or 28th part of their whole distance from it. And the diameter of the Circle in the middle space between those two Foci which they illuminate when they fall there on any plane, perpendicular to the Axis (which Circle is the least into which they can all be gathered) is about the 55th part of the diameter of the Aperture of the Glass. So that 'tis a wonder that Telescopes represent Objects so distinct as they do. But were all the Rays of Light equally refrangible, the Error arising only from the Spheri-

calness of the Figures of Glasses would be many hundred times less." (p. 83.)

"But it's farther to be noted, that the most luminous of the prismatick Colours are the yellow and orange. . . .The Images of Objects are therefore to be placed, not in the Focus of the mean refrangible Rays which are in the confine of green and blue, but in the Focus of those Rays which are in the middle of the orange and yellow; there where the Colour is most luminous and fulgent." (p. 85.)

"Now were it not for this different Refrangibility of Rays, Telescopes might be brought to a greater perfection than we have yet described, by composing the Object-Glass of two Glasses with Water between them." (p. 90.)

"And the Refractions on the concave sides of the Glasses, will very much correct the Errors of the Refractions on the convex sides, so far as they arise from the sphericalness of the Figure. And by this means might Telescopes by brought to sufficient perfection, were it not for the different Refrangibility of several sorts of Rays. But by reason of this different Refrangibility, I do not yet see any other means of improving Telescopes by Refractions alone than that of increasing their lengths, for which end the late contrivance of Hugenius seems well accommodated. . . .and the

Object-glass being fix'd upon a strong upright Pole becomes more steady." (p. 90.)

"Seeing therefore the Improvement of Telescopes of given lengths by Refractions is desperate; I contrived heretofore a Perspective by Reflexion, using instead of an object-glass a concave Metal. (p. 91.). . . ."Having thought of a tender way of polishing, proper for metal, whereby, as I imagined, the figure also would be corrected to the last; I began to try, what might be effected in this kind, and by degrees so far perfected an Instrument by which I could discern Jupiter's four Concomitants, and shewed them divers times to two others of my acquaintance. I could also discern the Moon-like phases of Venus, but not very distinctly, nor without some niceness in disposing the instrument." (Letter to the Royal Society). . . . "The diameter of the Sphere to which the metal was ground concave was about 25 English Inches, and by consequence the length of the Instrument about six Inches and a quarter. The Eye-glass was plano-convex, and the diameter of the Sphere to which the convex side was ground was about 1/5 of an Inch, or a little less, and by consequence it magnified between 30 and 40 times. By another way of measuring I found that it magnified about 36 times. The concave Metal bore an Aperture of an Inch and a third part. Two of these I made about 16 years ago and have one of them still by me." (p. 91.). . . ."The Polish I used was in this manner. I had two round Copper Plates each six inches in diameter, the one convex the other concave, ground very true to one another. On the convex I ground the Object-Metal till it had taken the Figure of the Convex. . . .Then I pitched over the surface very thinly by dropping melted Pitch upon it. . . .Then I took Putty which I had made very fine by washing it from all its grosser particles, and laying a little of this upon the Pitch, I ground it upon the Pitch with the con-cave Copper till it had done making a noise; and then upon the Pitch I ground the Object-Metal with a brisk motion, for about two or three Minutes, leaning hard upon it." (p. 93.)

No reflecting telescopes of any kind other than the two mentioned in the preceding quotations, were made by anyone, till Hadley began his work fifty-two years later, in 1723.

"If the Theory of making Telescopes could at length be fully brought into practice, yet there would be certain Bounds beyond which Telescopes could not perform. For the Air through which we look upon the Stars, is in a perpetual Tremor; as may be seen by the tremulous Motion of Shadows cast from high Towers and by the twinkling of the fix'd Stars. But these Stars do not twinkle when viewed through Telescopes which have large apertures. . . . The only remedy is a most serene and quiet Air, such as may perhaps be found on the tops of the highest Mountains above the grosser Clouds.'' (p. 98.)

It is interesting to note that some of the most important observatories are now located on mountain tops. The largest are the Lick Observatory on Mount Hamilton and the Mount Wilson Observatory, both in California. The largest telescope in the world is the 100-inch Newtonian Reflector of the Mount Wilson Observatory.

"To define the Refrangibility of the several sorts of homogeneal Lights answering to the several Colours. . . . I held the paper so that the Spectrum might fall upon this whilst an Assistant whose Eyes for distinguishing Colours were more critical than mine, did. . . . note the Confines of the Colours. . . . And this Operation being divers times repeated, I found that the Observations agreed well enough with one another. Let (certain lengths) . . . . be in proportion to one another, as the numbers 1, 8/9, 5/6, 3/4, 2/3, 3/5, 9/16, 1/2, and so to represent the Chords of a Key, and of a Tone, a third Minor, a fourth . . . . And the Intervals will be the spaces which the several Colours (red, orange, yellow, green, blue, indigo, violet) take up.'' (p. 110.)

"Whiteness and all grey Colours between white and black, may be compounded of Colours, and the whiteness of the Sun's Light is compounded of all the primary colours mix'd in a due proportion." (p. 117.)

"All the Colours in the Universe which are made by Light, and depend not on the Power of Imagination, are either the Colours of Homogenael Lights, or compounded of these,. . . ." (p. 138.)

"And these Theorems being admitted into Opticks there would be scope enough of handling that Science voluminously after a new manner." (pp. 109–114.)

The "Second Book of Opticks" begins with "Observations concerning the Reflexions, Refractions, and Colours of thin transparent Bodies," such as soap bubbles, thin plates of mica, films of water or air, and other bodies in the form of thin sheets. Boyle and Hooke had previously studied such colors, and had produced the colored circles of light, universally known today as "Newton's Rings". Newton made very careful and elaborate measurements of the sizes of the rings, thicknesses of the films, and of the relations of these quantities to the colors. He says:

"The Thicknesses of the Air between the Glasses there, where the Rings are successively made by the limits of the seven Colours, red, orange, yellow,

green, blue, indigo, violet in order, are to one
another as the "Cube Roots of the Squares of the
eight lengths of a Chord, which sound the Notes
in an eighth, sol, la, fa, sol, la, mi, fa, sol."
(p. 186.)

He returns repeatedly to this relation of the
spaces occupied by the several colors to "the
lengths of a Monochord which sound the Tones of
an Eight." (pp. 270, 280, 320.)

The ratios of these harmonies were thought by
some philosphers and astronomers, to furnish the
key to many of the mysteries of nature. Sir J. J.
Thomson remarks: "It was, I think, the siren's
song of these harmonies that lured Newton to this
false conclusion."

Newton believed that the seven colors were
seven distinct homogeneous unchangeable *kinds* of
light, and that the proportional space occupied by
each in the spectrum was due to an inherent property of the color. This would mean that the
spectrum given by one substance would be exactly
similar to that given by any other substance, and
that an achromatic lens is impossible. Newton
proceeds to develop a general theory of color by
which the colors of all natural bodies, solids, and
liquids, are produced in the same manner as are the
colors of thin plates.

"The least parts of almost all natural Bodies are

in some measure transparent. . . . . Between
the parts of opake and colour'd Bodies are many
Spaces, either empty or replenished with other
mediums: as Water between the tinging Corpuscles wherewith a Liquor is impregnated, Air
between the Globules that constitute Clouds or
Mists. . . . . The transparent parts of bodies
according to their several sizes reflect Rays of one
Colour, and transmit those of another, on the same
grounds that thin Plates or Bubbles do reflect or
transmit those Rays. And this I take to be the
ground of all their Colour. . . . . The bigness
of the component parts of natural Bodies may be
conjectured by their Colours. . . . . The azure
Colours of the Skies seem to be of this order."
(p. 232.)

"It is not impossible but that Microscopes may
at length be improved to the discovery of the
Particles of Bodies . . . . if they are not already
in some measure arrived to that degree of perfection. . . . . And by one that would magnify
three or four thousand times perhaps they might
all be discovered." (Newton thought that the
particles were of the same order of size as the length
of a "fit of easy transmission," while we now
believe them to be less than 1/1000th part of that
distance, and much too small to justify Newton's
theory.) (p. 236.)

"If Light be swifter in Bodies than in Vacuo in the proportion of the Sines which measure the Refraction of the Bodies, the Forces of the Bodies to reflect and refract Light, are very nearly proportional to the densities of the same Bodies, excepting that unctuous and sulphureous Bodies refract more than others of the same density." (p. 245.)

"Whence it seems rational to attribute the refractive Power of all Bodies chiefly, if not wholly, to the sulphureous parts with which they abound. For it's probable that all Bodies abound more or less with Sulphurs. And as Light congregated by a Burning-glass acts most upon sulphureous Bodies, to turn them into fire and Flame; so, since all action is mutual, Sulphurs ought to act most upon Light." (p. 250–251.)

"Light is propogated from luminous Bodies in time, and spends about seven or eight Minutes of an Hour in passing from the Sun to the Earth." (p. 252.)

"Rays of Light, by impinging on any refracting or reflecting Surface, excite vibrations in the refracting or reflecting Medium or Substance, and by exciting them agitate the solid parts of the refracting or reflecting Body, and by agitating them cause the Body to grow warm or hot; that the vibrations thus excited are propagated in the refracting or reflecting Medium or Substance, much

[32]

after the manner that vibrations are propagated in the Air for causing Sound, and move faster than the Rays so as to overtake them; and that when any Ray is in that part of the vibration which conspires with its Motion, it easily breaks through a refracting Surface, but when it is in the contrary part of the vibration which impedes its motion, it is easily reflected; and, by consequence, that every Ray is successively disposed to be easily reflected, or easily transmitted, by every vibration which overtakes it. But whether this Hypothesis be true or false I do not here consider." (p. 255–256.)

"The returns of the disposition of any Ray to be reflected I will call its Fits of easy Reflexion, and those of its disposition to be transmitted its Fits of easy Transmission, and the space it passes between every return and the next return, the Interval of its Fits." (p. 256.)

"If the Rays which paint the Colour in the confine of yellow and orange pass perpendicularly out of any Medium into Air, the Intervals of their Fits of easy Reflexion are the $\frac{1}{89000}$th part of an Inch. And of the same length are the intervals of their Fits of easy Transmission." (The "interval of the Fits" is clearly what is now called the wave-length. Newton's value is of the proper order of magnitude, but is only about half of the correct numerical value.) (p. 260.)

[33]

The "Third Book of Opticks" begins with observations concerning "The Inflexions of the Rays of Light and the Colours made thereby." He says:

"Grimaldo has inform'd us that if a beam of the Sun's Light be let into a dark Room through a very small hole, the Shadows of things in this Light will be larger than they ought to be . . . . I made in a piece of Lead a small Hole with a Pin, whose breadth was the 42nd part of an Inch. For 21 of those Pins laid together took up the breadth of half an Inch. . . . . Through this Hole I let into my darken'd Chamber a beam of the Sun's Light, and found that the Shadows of Hairs, Thread, Pins, Straws, and such like slender Substances placed in this beam of Light, were considerably broader than they ought to be, if the Rays of Light passed on by these Bodies in right Lines. (p. 292.)

"The Shadows of all Bodies (Metals, Stones, Glass, Wood, Horn, Ice, etc.) in this Light were border'd with three parallel Fringes or Bands of colour'd Light. . . . ." (p. 295.)

"I caused the edges of two Knives to be ground strait, and pricking their points into a Board so that their edges might look towards one another, and meeting near their points contain a rectilinear Angle, I fasten'd their Handles together with Pitch to make this angle invariable." (p. 304.)

[34]

The detailed explanations of the experiments on diffraction fill twenty pages of the book and conclude with this statement:

"When I made the foregoing Observations, I design'd to repeat most of them with more care and exactness, and to make some new ones for determining the manner how the Rays of Light are bent in their passage by Bodies for making the Fringes of Colours with the dark lines between them. But I was then interrupted, and cannot now think of taking these things into farther consideration. And since I have not finish'd this part of my Design, I shall conclude, with proposing only some Queries in order to farther search to be made by others." (p. 313.)

The queries are thirty-one in number, and, with the discussions, fill the concluding seventy pages of the treatise. Sir J. J. Thomson says: "In these abandons the severe, almost Euclidean style the earlier part of the book; he flings away his policy of 'Hypotheses non fingo;' he makes up for lost time." These queries treat largely of the theoretical explanations of the nature of light, but they also attempt to show an almost weird connection between physical facts and laws and metaphysical and theological speculations. A few quotations will be given from this curious mixture of physics and metaphysics.

"Query 1. Do not Bodies act upon Light at a distance, and by their action bend its Rays, and is not this action (CAETERIS PARIBUS) strongest at the least distance?" (p. 313.)

"Query 2. Do not the Rays which differ in Refrangibility differ also in Flexibility, and are they not by their different inflexions separated from one another, so as after separation to make the Colours in the three Fringes above described? And after what manner are they inflected to make those Fringes?" (p. 313.)

"Query 3. Are not the Rays of Light in passing by the edges and sides of Bodies, bent several times backwards and forwards, with a motion like that of an Eel? And do not the three Fringes of colour'd Light above mention'd, arise from three such bendings?" (p. 313.)

"Query 13. Do not several sorts of the Vibrations of several bignesses, according to their bignesses excite Sens: Newton Colours, much after the manner of the ations of the Air, according to their several bignesses excite Sensations of several Sounds?" (p. 320.)

"Query 14. May not the harmony and discord of Colour arise from the proportions of the Vibrations propagated through the Fibres of the optick Nerves into the Brain, as the harmony and discord

of Sounds arise from the proportions of the Vibrations of the Air?'' (p. 320.)

"Query 18. If in two large tall cylindrical Vessels of Glass inverted, two little Thermometers be suspended so as not to touch the Vessels, and the Air be drawn out of one of these Vessels, and these Vessels thus prepared be carried out of a cold place into a warm one; the Thermometer in vacuo will grow warm as much, and almost as soon as the Thermometer which is not in vacuo. . . . . Is not the Heat of the warm Room convey'd through the vacuum by the Vibrations of a much subtiler Medium than Air, which after the Air was drawn out remained in the Vacuum? And is not this Medium the same with that Medium by which Light is refracted and reflected, and by whose Vibrations Light communicates Heat to Bodies, and is put into Fits of easy Reflexion and easy Transmission? . . . . And is not this Medium exceedingly more elastick and active? and doth it not readily pervade all Bodies? And is it not (by its elastick force) expanded through all the Heavens?" (p. 323.)

"Query 22. May not Planets and Comets, and all gross Bodies, perform their Motions more freely, and with less resistance in this Aethereal Medium than in any Fluid, which fills all space adequately without leaving any Pores, and by consequence is much denser than Quick-silver or Gold? . . . . And so small resistance would scarce make any sensible alteration in the Motions of the Planets in ten thousand Years. If any one would ask how a Medium can be so rare, let him tell me how the Air, in the upper parts of the Atmosphere, can be above an hundred thousand times rarer than Gold . . . . And how the Effuvia of a Magnet can be so rare and subtile, as to pass through a Plate of Glass without any Resistance or Diminution of their Force, and yet so potent as to turn a magnetick Needle beyond the Glass." (p. 327.)

"Query 23. Is not Vision perform'd chiefly by the Vibrations of this medium. . . . . ." (p. 328.)

"Query 24. Is not Animal Motion perform'd by the Vibrations of this Medium excited in the Brain by the power of the Will. . . . . " (p. 328.)

"Query 25. Are there not other original properties of the Rays of Light, besides those already described? An instance of another original Property we have in the Refraction of Island Crystal. . . . . " (p. 328.)

"Query 26. Every Ray of Light has therefore two opposite Sides, originally endued with a Property on which the unusual Refraction depends, and the other two opposite Sides not endued with that Property. And it remains to be enquired, whether there are not more Properties of Light by which the Sides of the Rays differ, and are distinquish'd from one another." (p. 333.)

"Query 28. Are not all Hypotheses erroneous, in which Light is supposed to consist in Pression or Motion, propagated through a Fluid Medium? . . . . The main Business of Natural Philisophy is to argue from Phaenomena without feinging Hypotheses, and to deduce Causes from Effects, till we come to the very first Cause, which certainly is not mechanical. . . . . " (p. 336.)

"Query 29. Are not the Rays of Light very small Bodies emitted from shining Substances? For such Bodies will pass through uniform Mediums in right Lines without bending into the shadow, which is the Nature of the Rays of Light." (p. 345.) "Nothing more is requisite for producing all the variety of Colours and degrees of Refrangibility, than that the Rays of Light be Bodies of different Sizes, the least of which may make violet the weakest and darkest of the Colours, and be more easily diverted by refracting Surfaces from the right Course; and the rest as they are bigger and bigger, may make the stronger and more lucid Colours, blue, green, yellow and red, and be more and more difficultly diverted." (p. 397.) "I only say, that what ever it be, it's difficult to conceive

[39]

how the Rays of Light, unless they be Bodies, can have a permanent Virtue in two of their Sides which is not in their other Sides." (p. 348.)

"Query 30. Are not gross Bodies and Light convertible into one another, and may not Bodies receive much of their activity from the Particles of Light which enter their Composition? . . . . Eggs grow from insensible Magnitudes, and change into Animals; Tadpoles into Frogs: and Worms into Flies. All Birds, Beasts and Fishes, Insects, Trees, and other Vegetables, and their several parts, grow out of Water and Watery Tinctures and Salts, and by Putrefaction return again into watery Substances. And Water standing a few Days in the open Air, yields a Tincture, which (like that of Mault) by standing longer yields a Sediment and a Spirit, but before Putrefaction is fit Nourishment for Animals and Vegetables. And among such various and strange Transmutations, why may not Nature change Bodies into Light, and Light into Bodies?" (p. 350.)

"Query 31. (The consideration of this Query fills the last thirty-two pages of the Treatise, pp. 350–382.) "Have not the small Particles of Bodies certain Powers, Virtues or Forces, by which they act at a distance, not only upon the Rays of Light for reflecting, refracting and inflecting them, but also upon one another for producing a great

part of the Phaenomena of Nature?" (p. 350.)
"The Parts of all homogeneal hard Bodies which
fully touch one another, stick together very
strongly, and for explaining how this may be,
some have invented hooked Atoms, which is beg-
ging the Question; and others tell us that Bodies are
glued together by rest, that is, by an occult Quality,
or rather by nothing; and others, that they stick
together by conspiring Motions, that is, by relative
rest amongst themselves. I had rather infer from
their Cohesion, that their particles attract one
another by some Force, which in immediate Contact is exceeding strong, at small distances performs
the chemical Operations above mention'd, and
reaches not far from the Particles with any sensible
Effect." (p. 364.) "And it is the Business of
experimental Philosophy to find them out . . . .
All these things being consider'd it seems probable
to me, that God in the Beginning form'd Matter
in solid, massy, hard, impenetrable, movable
Particles, of such Sizes and Figures, and with such
other Properties, and in such Proportion to Space,
as most conduced to the End for which he form'd
them." (p. 375.) "For it became him who created them to set them in order. And if he did so,
it's unphilosophical to seek for any other Origin of
the World, or to pretend that it might arise out
of a Chaos by the mere Laws of Nature; though

[41]

being once form'd, it may continue by those Laws
for many Ages . . . . Such a wonderful Uniformity in the Planetary System must be allowed
the Effect of Choice.   And so must the Uniformity
in the Bodies of Animals, they having generally a
right and a left side shaped alike, and on either
side of their Bodies two Legs behind, and either
two Arms, or two Legs, or two Wings before upon
their Shoulders, and between their Shoulders a
Neck running down into a Back-bone, and a Head
upon it; and in the Head two Ears, two Eyes,
a Nose, a Mouth and a Tongue, alike situated.
Also the first Contrivance of those very artificial
parts of Animals, the Eyes, Ears, Brain, Muscles,
Heart, Lungs, Midriff, Glands, Larynx, Hands,
Wings, Swimming Bladders, Natural Spectacles,
and other Organs of Sense and Motion; and the
Instinct of Brutes and Insects, can be the effect
of nothing else than the Wisdom and Skill of
a powerful ever-living Agent, ... (p. 378.)
And if natural Philosophy in all its parts, by pur-
suing this Method, shall at length be perfected, the
Bounds of moral Philosophy will be also enlarged.
For so far as we can know by natural Philosophy
what is the first Cause, what Power he has over
us, and what Benefits we receive from him, so far our
Duty to him, as well as that towards one another,
will appear to us by the Light of Nature." (p. 381.)

[42]

It has been very generally stated that Newton adopted and developed the corpuscular theory of light, in which light consists of small particles and nothing else. This interpretation was really thrust upon him by his successors, for he was always exceedingly careful not to commit himself to any specific theory of the structure of light. Thirty years before his treatise appeared, when he was actively engaged in the optical researches, and was sending reports to the Royal Society, he wrote to Hooke, saying:

"Were I to propound an hypothesis it should be this, that light is something capable of exciting vibrations in the ether. They that will may suppose it an aggregate of various peripatetic qualities. Others may suppose it multitudes of unimaginable small and swift corpuscles of various sizes springing from shining bodies. . . . . But they that like not this may suppose light any other corporeal emanation, or any impulse or motion of any other medium or etherial spirit diffused through the main body of aether or what else they may imagine proper for their purpose. To avoid dispute and make this hypothesis general, let every man here take his fancy. . . . . "

However, it is very evident that Newton's final views involved, as a part of his theory, the corpuscular structure of rays of light. The general acclaim of the discovery of universal gravitation, and the prestige of the *Principia* gave Newton's views as to the nature of light general acceptance in preference to the undulatory theory supported by Hooke and Huygens, and this persisted for a hundred years. Then for another hundred years, the ether-wave theory completely superceded the corpuscular theory. When the quantum theory of radiation which involves something very like a corpuscular structure for light, was propounded by Planck in 1900, Newton's hypotheses acquired a curiously prophetic character, and were re-examined with keen interest. Whether a corpuscular theory, an ether theory, either one or both combined, will prevail when a Newton tercentenary is celebrated, one would not now venture to assert. The temptation to draw analogies between Newton's corpuscles and Planck's quanta and between "fits of easy transmission" and waves is confronted by difficulties so far insuperable, unless the new mechanics of Heisenberg and Schroedinger provides the necessary reconciliation.

It seems impossible at the present time to evaluate Newton's general theory of light; and his greatest direct contribution to optics, appears to be the discovery and explanation of the nature of color. He certainly laid the broad foundation upon which spectrum analysis rests, and out of this has come the new science of spectroscopy which is the most delicate and powerful method for the investigation of the structure of matter.

Newton's specific contributions to optics may be summarized as follows:

He discovered that sun light is a composite of different colors of different refrangibilities, and thus proved that color is a property of the light itself. He thought there were only seven definite homogeneous colors.

He explained the production of various colors and tints, including white and grey, by compounding the elementary colors.

He explained the colors of natural bodies, the colors of the spectrum, and of the rainbow.

He discovered that the defects of telescopes were due to chromatic abberation in the lenses.

He considered the effects of refraction, and concluded that the faults of telescopes could not be corrected by refraction, therefore, he gave his attention to the reflecting telescope.

He adopted a small flat, diagonal mirror for the reflecting telescope instead of the ellipsoidal small mirror proposed by Gregory, and he originated the use of a right-angled prism as a plane reflector.

He actually constructed with his own hands the first reflecting telescope, about six inches long. The mirror was of "speculum" metal prepared by himself, and he perfected the use of the pitch polisher. He constructed a second telescope, like the first, which was presented to the Royal Society.

He proposed the use of a mirror-glass reflector, but only one working through the glass.

He proposed a form of reflecting microscope, which, however, was not actually constructed.

He invented the sextant, the account of which was found in his papers, after his death, and after its reinvention by Hadley.

He made elaborate investigations of the colors of thin plates and films, and correctly analyzed the numerical relations of the phenomena which we call "Newton's Rings."

He studied the phenomena of diffraction, and of double refraction in crystals.

He considered at length, the arguments for and against the wave-theory of light, and concluded that light consists of corpuscles emitted by the source, which, when they are incident upon bodies produce vibrations in an all-prevading ether, and the effects of the ether-vibrations as well as the corpuscles must be taken into account.

It may not be amiss to specify a few things which Newton did not do. He did not discover "Newton's Rings" nor the colors of thin plates. Diffraction had been investigated by Grimaldi. The reflecting telescope had been correctly set forth by

Gregory. The formation of the rain-bow by reflection of light in the rain drops had been explained by Descartes but not in a manner to account for the varied colors.

Several phenomena which might have followed directly from Newton's discoveries were not detected by him. He failed to detect the continuous gradation of color, and did not detect the extension of the spectrum beyond the visible. He did not detect the variation in the ratio of dispersion to refraction in different substances. He did not propose the silver-on-glass reflecting telescope. He made no telescopes other than the two tiny models, one inch in diameter and six inches long. He did not recognize the wave-like nature of the "fits of easy transmission and reflecion," nor adopt the interference explanation for "Newton's Rings" and diffraction fringes. After inventing the sextant, he neglected to publish an account of it.

When an investigator is searching for things quite unknown, it would be both irrational and very ungenerous to blame him for what he does not find; we should only honor him for the discoveries he does make. Newton's contributions to optics are not as important as those set forth in the *Principia*, and are not greater than those of several other scientists, yet they surely secure him a place in the foremost rank of those who have founded our present system of optics.

The science of light today is indebted to Newton not alone for his discoveries in optics, but in a greater degree to his general influence upon the methods of philosophic thought. The discovery of universal gravitation is the discovery of the law of universal order, which is the basis and essential character of all science. The example of such profound and comprehensive philosophizing has been one of Newton's contributions to optics as well as to other sciences.

And now, two-hundred years after the death of Newton, in behalf of the science of optics, let us join the great chorus of all the sciences in doing reverence to him, not only for what he was, but for what he has been for these centuries, and for what he is now. We repeat the inscription on the Westminster tablet which was erected in 1731:

LET MEN REJOICE
THAT SO GREAT A GLORY OF THE HUMAN RACE
HAS APPEARED

NEWTON'S PHILOSOPHY OF GRAVITATION WITH SPECIAL REFERENCE TO MODERN RELATIVITY IDEAS

NEWTON'S PHILOSOPHY OF GRAVITATION WITH SPECIAL REFERENCE TO MODERN RELATIVITY IDEAS

GEORGE DAVID BIRKHOFF, Ph.D., D.Sc.

Professor of Mathematics, Harvard University

IT IS said that at the conclusion of a dinner given at the home of the English painter Haydon nearly a century ago, the poet Keats, raising his glass, proposed a toast to the confusion of Newton, and that Wordsworth, astonished, asked an explanation. Keats replied that Newton had destroyed the rainbow in reducing it to a prism. Today we honor Sir Isaac Newton for the very achievements which the poet deplored.

Following immediately upon the optical discoveries alluded to by Keats, came the great achievements of Newton in the theory of gravitation. In order to understand the advance which he made, it is necessary to recall briefly what had been done before his time, and at what stage his contemporaries had arrived, when he announced the law of gravitation.

Up to the time of the ancient Greeks, scientifically-minded men had accumulated comparatively few experimental facts. These lay mainly in the

fields of elementary optics, mechanics and astronomy. Thus Euclid wrote two books on the optical
properties of light and its reflection from mirrors;
Archimedes stated correctly the mechanical principles of the lever and the equilibrium of floating
bodies; and Ptolemy wrote an elaborate astronomical treatise. It was astronomy, however, that was
pursued with most success.

For the description of all these facts as well as
those of every day life, the concepts of space and
time, which seemed self-evident, were available.
This concept of space is incorporated in ordinary
geometry, while the concept of measurable absolute
time was so immediate that it went unquestioned
by physicists and philosophers until the discovery
of the theory of relativity by Einstein. Using
this apparently inevitable structure of space and
time, it was possible to formulate the observed
laws with exactitude.

As soon as a sufficient number of astronomical
facts had been obtained, it was perceived that the
sun, moon and planets were large spherical bodies
like the earth, and that their motions, and the
motions of the stars, despite a superficial simplicity
to the casual observer, were bewilderingly irregular
in detail. Here was offered a fascinating mystery
of the heavens which some of the greatest minds
were bound to attempt to unravel.

The idea that the sun might be the central body instead of the earth is one of great antiquity. Nevertheless scientific thought before Copernicus took the earth to be absolutely at rest. The task of explaining the motions of the heavenly bodies relatively to the earth proved to be exceedingly difficult, and gave rise to the concept of motion in epicycles. This sufficed for the mere description of many of the facts, but in no way unified or explained them.

Early in the sixteenth century Copernicus published the theory known by his name, according to which the space attached to the sun and fixed stars, rather than the space attached to the earth, is "at rest" or "absolute." He effected thereby a remarkable simplification in the explanation of the observed facts. On the basis of this theory Kepler was not only able to discover the laws of motion of the planets about the sun, but also came to have vague but essentially correct ideas concerning a gravitational force of attraction which kept the earth, moon and planets in their orbits.

Furthermore his great contemporary Galileo, who all but invented the telescope, and made remarkable discoveries with it, established the fact that it was not change of place so much as change of velocity which measured force; thus, a body not acted upon by forces would move with constant

velocity in a straight line.   The essential elements
of modern dynamical law must be attributed to
Galileo.

Kepler went so far as to conjecture that the law
of attraction according to the inverse second power
of the distance might hold.   It was primarily the
lack of suitable mathematical instruments of
thought which stood in the way of further development.   Without the analytic geometry of
Descartes and the infinitesimal calculus of Newton
and Leibnitz, the solution of the problem was
impossible.

Thus it is not surprising that Halley, Sir Christopher Wren and Hooke in England were considering the possibility that this law might hold, almost
simultaneously, with Newton.   Halley wrote to
Newton on June 29, 1686, concerning this matter as
follows:

"And I know to be true that in January (16) 83/4
I, having from the consideration of the sesquialter
proportion of Kepler, concluded that the centripe-
tall force decreased in the proportion of the squares
of the distances reciprocally, came one Wednesday
to town, where I met with Srs. Christ. Wrenn and
Mr. Hook, and, falling in discourse about it, Mr.
Hook affirmed that upon that principle all the laws
of celestiall motions were to be demonstrated, and
that he himself had done it.   I declared the ill

success of my attempts; and Sr. Christopher, to encourage the inquiry, s^{d} that he would give Mr. Hook or me two months time to bring him a convincing demonstration thereof, and besides the honour, he of us that did it, should have from him a present of a book of 40^{2}''.

However, Newton far surpassed his contemporaries in mathematical power as well as in physical insight. He was the first to triumph over the purely mathematical difficulties involved. In my opinion it is this which constitutes his greatest achievement rather than the first formulation of the law of gravitation, or of the laws of motion, both known by his name today.

It is worthy of note that Newton himself held this point of view. His able but jealous rival Hooke felt that the discovery was his own, merely because he had announced the law. But Newton considered that there was very little merit in Hooke's unverified conjecture. In the letter to his friend Halley, written June 20, 1686, to which Halley's letter replied, he said sarcastically in regard to Hooke's attitude:

"Now is not this very fine? Mathematicians that find out, settle, and do all the business, must content themselves with being nothing but dry calculators and drudges; and another that does nothing but pretend and grasp at all things must carry away all the invention, as well as of those that were to follow him, as of those that went before."

In his great *Principia* of 1687 Newton took all of these questions out of the realm of nebulous speculation and gave them their classical mathematical form. This work may justly be regarded as the most important single contribution to physics that has ever been made. With its publication there was begun a period of more than two centuries in which it was sought to reduce all physics to Newtonian dynamics. In the *Principia* Newton not only showed by rigorous mathematical deduction how the gravitational law of inverse squares led to the empirically determined laws of Kepler, but he gave a satisfactory dynamical explanation of many known facts about the motions of the heavenly bodies, the tides, etc. His treatment of the irregularities of the moon's motion is exceedingly remarkable.

The basic elements in Newton's theory of space, time and gravitation are easily stated. The first scholium of his *Principia* shows that he adhered to the customary notion of absolute space and absolute time:

"I. Absolute, true, and mathematical time, of itself, and from its own nature flows equably without regard to anything external, and by another name is called duration; relative, apparent, and common time is some sensible and external (whether accurate or unequable) measure of duration by means of motion. . . . .

"II. Absolute space, in its own nature, without regard to anything external, remains always similar and immovable. Relative space is some movable dimension or measure of the absolute space.

"III. Place is a part of space which a body takes up, and is according to the space, either absolute or relative.

"IV. Absolute motion is the translation of a body from one absolute place into another; and relative motion, the translation from one relative place into another."

There was then for Newton, as for all his predecessors, a particular absolute space and absolute time which formed the background with reference to which physical events were described. For the ancients the space attached to the earth was absolute; for Copernicus, the space attached to the sun and fixed stars; for Newton, the space defined by the center of gravity of the solar system.

What is the rôle of an absolute space? It must be a particular space in terms of which the explanation of physical laws is most simply given.

But the laws formulated by Newton were in reality such as to make no distinction between the space attached to the center of gravity of the solar system, and that attached to the center of gravity of any other isolated system of bodies. In fact it became impossible to distinguish the space which he called absolute from any other space moving uniformly with respect to it in some fixed direction. Thus there is in fact a spatial relativity present in his dynamics, which he felt vaguely, as the following statement from the same scholium bears witness:

"It is indeed a matter of great difficulty to discover and effectively distinguish the true motions of particular bodies from the apparent; because the parts of that immovable space in which those motions are performed do by no means come under the observation of our senses. Yet the thing is not altogether desperate. . . . ."

Apparently Newton conceived of his absolute space as filled by an ethereal medium, by the aid of which he hoped to be able to determine absolute motion.

As a first approximation to the facts of nature, the Newtonian dynamics, with its spatial relativity, is likely to stand permanently. It is the simplest theory which explains the main facts. The gravitational theory which is the cornerstone of his dynamics will stand for the same reason. We still teach our students elementary mechanics and gravitation on the Newtonian basis.

It is desirable to emphasize the simplicity and naturalness of the Newtonian law of gravitation, as well as the degree of exactitude with which it accounts for the observed facts. Once the Copernican theory is grasped, it is seen that the gravitational forces must act directly between the bodies concerned, just as bodies are pulled directly towards the earth by its gravitation. Moreover such force must diminish as the mutual distance increases, but whether inversely as the first power of the distance, as the second power, or as some higher power is not so plain. However Kepler's third law of motion indicates at once that only the second power is admissible; this fact was established by Huyghens in 1673.

It is decidedly interesting to consider the somewhat philosophic principles which led Newton and his contemporaries to the proper formulation of the gravitational law. No one has formulated these principles more admirably than Newton himself at the beginning of the third volume of his *Principia*, or "rules of reasoning in philosophy." These have been summarized as follows:

"*Rule I*. We are not to assume more causes than are sufficient and necessary for the explanation of the observed facts.

Rule II. Hence as far as possible similar effects

must be assigned to the same causes; *ex. gr.*, the fall of stones in Europe and America.

Rule III. Properties common to all bodies within reach of our experiments are to be assumed as pertaining to bodies; *ex. gr.*, extension.

Rule IV. Properties in experimental philosophy obtained by wide induction are to be regarded as accurate, or at least very nearly true, until phenomena or experiments show that they may be corrected or are liable to exceptions."

These principles remain as unexceptionable today as they were at the time of Newton. Newton's scientific procedure was in strict accordance with these principles. He marshalled the facts then known concerning the phenomenon of gravitation, and gave a satisfactory explanation of them. His theory was the simplest one available, and any more elaborate theory would have been a useless and unjustified flight of the imagination.

What is it then that has forced us to progress beyond the Newtonian point of view to the next stage in the development of our notions concerning space, time and gravitation?

In answering this question very briefly, it is interesting to recall first of all that even in Newton's day a certain amount of criticism was made of his law of gravitation because it allowed one body to affect another body, however distant, instantaneously. Action at a distance seemed to disturb a good many of the natural philosophers of that day, and Leibnitz in particular criticised Newton's theory on that basis. Newton himself felt it necessary to offer some justification of his law, and at the end of the third volume of the *Principia* will be found some speculations as to the possibility of explaining gravitation by means of an all pervading ethereal medium. Undoubtedly the fact, discovered by Römer in 1675, that light travels with a large but finite velocity lent force to this criticism. But Laplace showed later that if gravitational forces did travel with a finite velocity, the velocity would be at least ten times that of light. Hence this objection to the theory seemed out of harmony with the experimental results.

The fact that light was propagated at a finite velocity was indeed of extraordinary significance from the philosophic point of view. It meant that events were not seen when they happened. The apparent simultaneity of events appeared as an illusion. Thus the related notions of simultaneity and absolute time no longer could be based upon the immediate evidence of the senses. However, this fact alone would never have sufficed to lead to the modern point of view. The modification has been brought about by the steady accumulation of new experimental results in physics. After the work of Faraday and Maxwell the rôle of electricity and magnetism in nature began to appear to be more and more fundamental. Not only was light discovered to be an electromagnetic manifestation, but the atom was found to be governed by electromagnetic laws. The dynamical behavior of visible bodies began to be regarded as merely the statistical result of the electrodynamic behavior of their atomic constituents. The conjecture inevitably arose that the physical universe is fundamentally electromagnetic, that the velocity of light is a limiting velocity in nature. The Newtonian law of gravitation could only be regarded as accurate when the bodies concerned were moving at velocities small compared with that of light.

One outcome of this modified view of the physical universe has been the gravitational theory of relativity, discovered by Einstein in 1915. In it space and time are taken to be fundamentally conditioned by the presence of matter, and gravitation appears as the inevitable consequence of this interconnection. If the new theory accounts for some of the slight discrepancies of the Newtonian theory, and is more sound from a general philosophic point of view, it is at the same time less simple, and perhaps less secure of a permanent place in physics, since the Newtonian theory will always hold its position as the proper first approximation. On the other hand, it appears to be certain that the general influence of the theory of relativity will remain, and that the classical view of space and time as a final explanation has been permanently abandoned.

It is worthy of note that the theory of relativity of Einstein appears as the simplest possible mathematical theory which can be built up consonantly with the electromagnetic structure alluded to above, and which takes space and time to be conditioned by matter. The theory of Einstein offers amazing contrasts with that of Newton. Space and time are no longer separate, but are joined together in a four-dimensional space-time. The fundamental elements are no longer points and instants of time, but are events, defined by a point-at-an-instant. Absolute time and simultaneity no longer exist, but only a local time at each particle.

Like the Newtonian theory, the theory of Einstein is only successful in explaining gravitational phenomena. It throws no light on any other part of physics. Moreover there is as yet no indication as to precisely how the Newtonian mechanics is to be explained in terms of a more fundamental relativistic mechanics of the atom.

As a matter of fact, we have now reached a

stage in which no theories appear to be fundamental in physics—it is merely that some are more fundamental than others in certain directions. Although we have a vague feeling of the unity of the physical universe, and are in possession of beautiful mathematical abstractions which account for numerous phenomena, nevertheless we have just begun to discover what is going on. The scientist of today, equally as well as Newton, can say "I do not know what I may appear to the world; but to myself I seem to have been only like a boy playing on the sea-shore, and diverting myself in now and then finding a smoother pebble or a prettier shell than ordinary, while the great ocean of truth lay all undiscovered before me."

NEWTON'S INFLUENCE UPON THE DEVELOPMENT OF ASTROPHYSICS

NEWTON'S INFLUENCE UPON THE DEVELOPMENT OF ASTROPHYSICS

WILLIAM WALLACE CAMPBELL, Sc.D., LL.D.

President of the University of California and Director of the Lick Observatory

THE subject of astronomy divides naturally into two fields, though here and there the fields overlap.

First, there is the astronomy of position, sometimes called astrometry. Astrometry has always been saying:

> "Twinkle, twinkle, little star,
> How I wonder *where* you are;"

also, where have you been, and where are you going?

The second division of the astronomical field is known as astrophysics—the physics of the stars. It treats of their brightness, their temperatures, their spectra, the evolutionary processes which attend their development from the time of their birth to their extreme old age. Astrophysics is primarily concerned with responding to Jane Taylor's *actual* exclamation,

> "Twinkle, twinkle, little star,
> How I wonder *what* you are."

[67]

In answering the earnest inquiries about the stars, *where* you are, and *what* you are, a fine degree of progress has been made. But the still greater question concerning the stars, expressed in the exclamation, How I wonder *why* you are—why you exist at all, how you came into existence—this question remains very largely unanswered.

As the rich field of electrical science and art has developed from the discoveries made by such pioneers as Volta and Faraday, so the devotees of astronomical science regard Sir Isaac Newton as incomparably the greatest of their pioneers.

Newton's law of gravitation, while its principal applications relate to the astrometry of the universe, is rendering constant service to those who are trying to solve the problems of astrophysics: as an instrument of prediction and deduction; as an agency of interpretation; and as a check upon hypotheses. I shall give a few illustrations from the long list of available cases.

Our sun, an ordinary star, our own particular star, 866,000 miles in diameter, is believed to be gaseous from surface to center. The materials composing it are held in captivity, within its essentially spherical body, by the force of gravity, which does the uttermost demanded and permitted by Newton's law of gravitation to pull each atom in the sun toward the sun's center. The inward tendency is resisted by two well-recognized expansive forces, and possibly by other forces not yet discovered. At every point within the sun the resultant gravitational force, directed toward the center, and the resultant radiation pressure and the resultant elastic force of the gases, both directed away from the center, are in equilibrium. Because of the enormous mass of material, all of it constantly urged to get to the center, the pressure at the center of the sun is known, from Newton's law of gravitation, to be in excess of six million tons (American tons) per square inch. The temperature of the gases at the center probably lies somewhere between the limits eighteen and seventy million degrees on the Fahrenheit scale. At this temperature, if we may trust our processes of extrapolation, the elasticity of the simple gases there existing—their power of resisting compression into a solid or liquid state—is apparently all but sufficient to bear the load. The elasticity's Lilliputian assistant, known as radiation pressure—the pressure exerted by heat and light radiations on all surrounding matter upon which these radiations fall—offers, Eddington estimates, an addition of about 5 per cent to the expansive effort, amounting at the sun's center to at least 300,000 tons per square inch. If the force of gravity were eliminated from the sun, that body would expand with startling speed and to startling dimensions; and what is true of our sun is equally true of all other stars. Without Newton's law of gravitation, we should seek in vain to understand the conditions which exist within the stars; we could not hope ever to comprehend the processes of stellar evolution. Research in this large section of the astrophysical field makes unending use of Newton's law.

The law of gravitation has enabled us to draw certain important conclusions as to the conditions existing within the comets. It enables us to determine the orbits of our accurately observed meteors—the so-called shooting stars—and likewise the orbits of the comets. It enables us to say that the countless members of five or more meteor groups are known to be moving in the same orbits, respectively, as five or more well-known comets which have completely disappeared, and that the meteors in each group are distributed along the orbit of their maternal comet. It is but a simple step to the conclusion that the head of a comet is chiefly a great collection of small, separate, solid particles traveling together in an orbit around the sun;—probably billions of separate little bodies. When the comet is at a great distance from the Sun, the mutual attractions of the multitude of little bodies suffice to keep them together. When the comet is near the sun, the sun's attraction upon the small bodies nearest to the sun is stronger than it is upon the small bodies on the side of the comet farthest away from the sun, with the result, in due time, that the nearer meteoric bodies forge ahead of the main central mass, and the farther ones lag behind. The small bodies will eventually be distributed along the orbit, and the comet, because of this scattering, will become too faint to be visible from the earth.

Newton's law of gravitation enabled its author, first of all people, to prove that the distant stars, like our sun, are shining by virtue of their own light, and not by reflected light. Unless they were many hundreds of times as far away as the most distant planet then known in our system—Saturn— they must either be drawn into our sun, or show evidences of motion in orbits around the sun. The stars could not be observed to change their positions. Therefore they were very far away. However, at such great distances as would be necessary to prevent them from showing orbital motion they could not be seen from the earth if they were shining by reflected light. Therefore they must be shining by their own light, and be comparable in size with our sun.

Vastly more effective than the law of gravitation in enabling astrophysicists to answer the questions of what the stars are, in spectrum analysis. It is never really safe to say that any one thing is more important than any other thing, unless we agree to shut out the future. But certainly spectrum analysis as a means of interpreting and understanding the stars and other celestial bodies has been incomparably more effective, up to the present time, than any other method or system of approach to their mysteries. Isaac Newton was uniquely the pioneer of spectrum analysis. In January, 1666, when he was but twenty-three years and one month of age, two months after his discovery of the principles of the differential calculus, and two months before his discovery of the principles of the integral calculus, he discovered that white light—sunlight—is not simple and homogeneous in structure; white light contains ingredient lights of many colors: red, orange, yellow, green, blue, indigo, violet—the colors of the rainbow. When a ray of sunlight is passed through a prism of transparent material, say of glass—Newton may at first have used a prism composed of plane-glass surface plates and salt-water filling—the emergent rays are of different colors, and are bent from their courses in different degrees: the violet are refracted the most, the red the least; the seven principal colors, as listed above, running together, two by two, and forming a continuous spectrum. The cautious and thoughtful Newton found that the sending of one short section of the spectrum, say the red or the yellow, through a second prism, did not result in a renewed separation of this beam into many colors. The image remained red, or yellow, respectively. Also the sending of the multi-colored beam of light through a second prism, inverted with reference to the first prism, reunited the beam into its original size and white color. These simple elemental facts are the basis of spectrum analysis. Growing out of these discoveries, added to by Wollaston, Fraunhofer, Kirchhoff and hundreds of others, are the spectroscope, and especially the spectrograph, which have enabled astronomers to accomplish so much in the way of understanding the celestial objects.

About ninety years ago the celebrated French philosopher, Auguste Comte, published the dictum that we shall never be able to determine the chemical composition of the stars because we cannot reach up to the stars and bring fragments of them into our chemical laboratories for analysis. A quarter century later Rutherfurd and Secchi and Huggins and others were determining the composition of the stars—of the outer strata or atmospheres thereof—in terms of our well known chemical elements. Shortly thereafter this method of analysis was applied also to the comets and certain classes of the nebulae. And those were merely the beginnings of this wonder-working activity.

Briefly stated, the spectrograph, attached to a telescope, makes a star, or a nebula, or a comet write its own story upon the photographic plate: the true story of the conditions existing within it at the present time (*i.e.*, at the time when the light left the star); some of the leading facts about the star's size, its distance, its motion, its age in relation to the ages of other stars; something about its history, its peculiarities, and so on. Provided it sends to us enough light to work upon, it matters not whether the star be only five light years from us, or a thousand light years, or a million light years: the spectrograph and photographic plate receive and record the messages which it sends, telling, perhaps not all about itself, but certainly a very great deal about itself. And how are these remarkable powers related to Sir Isaac Newton? A few sentences will suffice to tell us.

Let us supposed that the one million books which are to compose a great library are thrown into a compact pile in the center of the floor of the library reading room: look at the heap of books as intently as we please, we cannot safely say anything about that library except possibly to guess at the number of volumes it contains. Suppose, now, we are interested in knowing all about the sizes of the books—their height, let us say. The librarian has them placed on the shelves in the order of their lengths, beginning with the shortest volume at one end of the shelving and running on with longer and longer volumes through the miles and miles of shelving, until finally the tallest book in the collection closes the series. By surveying the line of books we can determine what volumes of any given height are present in superabundance, or are scarce, or are entirely lacking. In the same manner the image of a star, as received in the eyepiece of a telescope, is an exceedingly minute point of light, into which have been combined light rays having a very great variety and range of colors and wave lengths. By looking at that image you can form not nearly so reliable an opinion of the characteristics of the star as an observer of the jumbled pile of books on the library floor could the library's richness or poverty on any subject, say the Napoleonic wars, or steamships, or Timbuctoo. Now, by using Newton's prism intelligently and accurately, the light rays which the telescope, left to itself, would pile upon each other in hopeless confusion, will be drawn out into a long, narrow line of light, violet at one end (the end of shorter light waves) and red at the other end (the end of longer light

[75]

waves), the other colors and wave lengths located in between the violet and the red, and *arranged in absolutely perfect order*. Not a single mistake as to orderly arrangement will be made. Let us now pass to the photographic image of this spectrum,— the very real and dependable message which the star has itself written for our information on the photographic plate. Examining the delicate image in detail by means of a microscope, we see that we are not dealing with a smooth, continuous image; there will usually be many places in the long narrow image at which there are vacancies, or absences of light. Such vacancies are known as dark lines, or absorption lines, in the spectrum. For different stars, the dark lines in the spectrum may vary from almost none, say two or three, up to many hundreds, or even thousands.

In the spectra of certain stars and nebulae, in the spectra of most comets, in the spectrum of the aurorae, we find many places at which the light rays exist in superabundance; and such intensified points in the spectra are known as bright lines, or emission lines. Now all of these dark lines and bright lines, which exist in almost endless variety of intensities and combinations, are full of significance. By their means the celestial bodies tell us their several true stories. Can we read their language, their hieroglyphics, and understand them? Yes, in admirable and satisfying degree, thanks to the spectroscopic Rosetta stones which Kirchhoff and his successors in the physical laboratories have been discovering for us in the last sixty-eight years—since the year 1859, the year also of Darwin's *Origin of Species*.

If we see absorption lines occupying several perfectly definite positions in the spectrum of the star, we know, as positively as we know anything, that hydrogen in the form of a gas is prominently present in the star's atmosphere, *i.e.*, in the outer strata of the star. If we see a great number of dark lines in certain perfectly definite positions in the spectrum, we know that iron in the form of iron vapor is present in the star. And so on for a long list of our other chemical elements. From the evidence supplied by spectrum analysis, we are convinced that the chemical elements which compose the earth exist also in our sun, and in general in the other stars, to the remotest parts of the visible universe.

When we observe the spectrum of the average comet we find, chiefly, that it duplicates the spectrum of our sun, which convinces us that a comet's light consists largely of reflected sunlight; but, in addition, the presence of certain bright lines in the comet's spectrum say to us that atoms of carbon and nitrogen and oxygen and sodium are present in the comet, and in response to some influence exerted upon them by the sun are themselves radiating light.

When we see that all of the lines in a star's spectrum, as photographed, are minutely shifted toward the red from their normal positions, we know that the star is moving away from us; and, if we measure the displacement of the lines, we may, from these measured displacements, compute the velocity of recession of the star. When the lines are all displaced a small amount toward the violet end of the spectrum, we know that the star, as the source of light, is moving toward us; and accurate measurements of the displacements will enable us to say with what speed the star is coming nearer to us. Through the use of these principles, a few of the larger telescopes in the world, with spectrographs attached to them, have determined the velocities of approach and recession of some four thousand stars distributed over the entire sky.

When we observe certain combinations of spectral lines we say that the star concerned is a Class K star; but I must not stop to tell you what a Class K star is. The stars in general are divided, at present, on the basis of their different types of spectra, into Classes O, B, A, F, G, K, M, R, N, S, with many subdivisions. Nearly all the stars can be arranged, as to their spectra, in a fairly continuous sequence, and this sequence is confidently believed to bear an intimate relationship to the evolutionary processes which attend the development of the stars, from their childhood, through middle age, old age, and on unto inability to shine any longer by means of their own light.

When in the spectrum of a star, say of a Class K star, certain dark lines are relatively strong and certain others are relatively weak, we know that the star is a giant among its brethren. Now we know quite satisfactorily how much light an average giant K star is radiating. If it were at a unit distance from us, we should expect to see it as a star of a certain magnitude. We actually see it as of a certain other brightness. The solution of a simple equation tells us, with an average error not exceeding 15 or 20 per cent, how far away the star is.

Similarly, if certain spectral lines are relatively faint, and other critical lines in the same spectrum are relatively strong, we know we are dealing with a dwarf star. If it is a Class G dwarf, for example, we can state with fair accuracy the magnitude which the star would have if it were at unit distance. We observe it to have a certain apparent brightness. The solution of a simple equation enables us to determine, with an error usually not exceeding 25 per cent, how far away the dwarf star is. In this manner astronomers, especially Adams, have been able to estimate, with a considerable degree of accuracy, the actual sizes and distances of more than two thousand stars.

In countless other ways: with the very numerous spectroscopic binary stars; with the so-called new stars; with the formless, planetary and spiral nebulae; with the zodiacal light; with all of the many kinds of variable stars; with the atmospheres of Mars and our other planets;—the spectrograph has made contributions to our understanding of the celestial bodies, in kind and degree truly remarkable.

Newton's discovery of the composite nature of sunlight was made in a most interesting manner.

It was known before Newton's day that a telescope equipped with a single glass lens having spherical surfaces was almost useless for the making of astronomical observations of any pretensions. Satisfactory images could not be obtained; the rays passing through the outer parts of such a lens would be brought to focus a little before the rays from the innermost areas of the lens. This result was called the spherical aberration of a lens. While experimenting with such a lens, Newton discovered another property, known as the chromatic aberration of a lens—that, even though a lens be altered slightly from the spherical form to bring all stellar rays of the same precise color or wave length to a common focus, the rays of different colors will not come into focus. We have known for more than a century that the use of two lenses in one telescopic object-glass, one made from light crown glass and the other from flint glass, permits the optician to bring a considerable stretch of the spectrum into satisfactory focus; say the yellow rays and a little of the adjacent orange and green sections, if a telescope is to be used visually; or the blue rays and a little of the adjoining (indigo-) violet section, if the telescope is to be used photographically. The use of three or four or more separate lenses of selected glass will enable longer and longer stretches of the spectrum of a star to be combined into a sharp point-image; but the use of many lenses is objectionable, not only by reason of higher cost, but chiefly because the extra lens surfaces cause the loss of more light by reflection, and the extra thickness of glass increases the loss by absorption. Newton erroneously thought that all prisms producing the same deviation for a selected color would give spectra of the same lengths; and therefore that the putting of a second lens into a telescopic object-glass could not be made to correct the chromatic aberration introduced by the first lens. In this he was mistaken, and he thereby narrowly missed discovering the principles of the achromatic refracting telescope. In search of perfect telescopic images, he transferred his interests to reflecting telescopes.

Newton recalled the theoretical descriptions, by Messenne in 1639 and by James Gregory in 1662, of the reflecting form of telescope, an instrument without lenses, but equipped with a mirror whose surface is accurately curved to the paraboloidal form, and highly polished. In 1668, when he was under twenty-six years of age, Newton, with his own hands, constructed the first reflecting telescope that ever existed. Its mirror, composed of speculum metal, was in diameter $1\frac{1}{4}$ inch, and in focal length $6\frac{1}{4}$ inches. He used this reflecting telescope upon Jupiter and his satellites, as well as upon other objects; and he sent it to the Royal Society in London for exhibition purposes. It is a far cry from Newton's $1\frac{1}{4}$-inch reflecting telescope to the 100-inch reflector of the Mount Wilson Observatory. The ratio of the surface areas of the two mirrors is about as 1 to 6500. Following the discovery of methods for the achromatizing of refracting telescopes, which occurred a full one hundred years after Newton's passing, reflecting telescopes fell almost completely into disuse; and it was in the closing years of the nineteenth century that the epoch-making discoveries resulting from Keeler's use of the 36-inch Crossley reflecting telescope: first, the enormous number of nebulae certainly existing in the heavens, but not yet observed; and, secondly, the astonishing number of spiral nebulae in existence, and, as Keeler commented, their undoubted importance in theories of cosmogony—it was then that astronomers in general realized the tremendous advantages of great reflecting telescopes for certain kinds of celestial photography, and became ambitious to possess them.

It was Newton who experimented with alloys of a few metals in search for the best alloy to compose telescope mirrors. His alloy of copper and tin was used for the mirrors of reflecting telescopes through the two succeeding centuries, with composition essentially unchanged.

Sir Isaac Newton was the first to use pitch and rouge as the materials for giving to telecope mirrors their final surface figures and polish. These are the materials still used by our makers of mirrors, prisms, flats, lenses, etc.,—without change from Newton's day to this.

Concerning the origin of the stars, and stellar evolution, Newton wrote:

"It seems to me that, if the matter of our sun and planets and all the matter of the universe were evenly scattered . . . . throughout infinite space, it would never convene into one mass; but some of it would convene into one mass and some into another, so as to make an infinite number of great masses, scattered great distances from one to another throughout all that infinite space. And thus might the sun and fixed stars be formed, supposing the matter were of a lucid nature.''

Newton failed to realize that the violent coming together of countless masses to form any one of the stellar bodies would generate heat, and therefore lucidity; but otherwise his views are, in general outline, in accord with those held today concerning the origin and formation of the stars.

Newton's result for the distance of an average first-magnitude star was criticised by some of his contemporaries, who made the objection that he had not allowed for any loss of starlight in its passage through space. Without absorption loss, the light coming to us from a star, his critics said, would be stronger than we observe it; therefore, the star is really nearer to us than Newton found it to be. Newton replied that there appears to be no appreciable loss by space absorption. If there were such loss, he said, we could not see many stars—only the nearer ones—because the absorption of their light, if absorption existed, would render the fairly distant stars wholly invisible. This general conclusion, that there is no appreciable loss of a star's light during its passage through clear space, enjoys universal acceptance today. Obstruction there is to the passage of light radiations by intervening materials; but we have no evidence that what we may call "pure space," whether filled by a medium arbitrarily named *ether*, or unfilled, charges any toll for the passage of light waves or light corpuscles through it.

It is not unreasonable to think that Nature's apparent failure to charge toll for transmitting light had something to do with Newton's final *preference* for the corpuscular theory of light. According to his own First Law of motion a body moving in a given direction with a given speed will continue so to move unless and until acted upon by an outside force. Therefore, a corpuscle of light traveling from a distant star should reach us with strength absolutely undiminished if it traveled exclusively through free space; but it is difficult to understand why a unit of light energy should arrive in full original strength if transmitted through intervening space by wave notion.

However, it would be a mistake to accredit Newton with the hypothesis that all light and heat are corpuscular, or that any light or heat is exclusively corpuscular; *i.e.*, consisting wholly of a shower of excessively minute particles shot out from the light and heat sources, such as the sun and the stars. His views as to the nature of light seem to have much in common with those held by physicists in the last two or three years—by de Broglie, Schroedinger, and others. Astrophysicists are deeply anxious to learn the correct answers to the questions: Just what is light? for they would like to know precisely how a star loses mass, apparently, by the radiation of its energy. Just what is radiation pressure? Just what is it that comes from the sun into our upper atmosphere, and causes the aurorae, the magnetic storms, and so on? There appears to be reason for hope that the physicists' knowledge of the structure of light and heat will in due time be so extended and perfected that the astrophysicists may use this knowledge to explain and predict the transformations which attend the lives of the stars and the other celestial objects.

To me it is clear that Sir Isaac Newton, easily the greatest man of physical science in historic times, was uniquely the great pioneer of astrophysics.

NEWTON'S DYNAMICS

NEWTON'S DYNAMICS

MICHAEL IDVORSKY PUPIN, Ph.D., Sc.D., LL.D.

Professor of Electro-mechanics, Columbia University

THE bicentennial commemoration of Newton's death turns our thoughts to his great achievements, and the greatest of them is his science of dynamics. This achievement is the crown of the scientific endeavors of the two centuries which preceded Newton. Both Columbus and Copernicus stand at the portal through which these two glorious centuries entered into the history of modern science. Newton's dynamics is the end of the first chapter of this history.

The discovery of America was the final experimental demonstration that our earth is a terrestrial globe, and it is highly probable that Columbus by this demonstration encouraged Copernicus in his speculations concerning the motions of heavenly bodies. Copernicus did not discover a new planetary system. Encouraged by the Columbus experiment he resurrected an ancient knowledge of the Arab astronomers relating to the figure of the earth and made it a part of the old planetary scheme first suggested by the Pythagoreans. But he did this at the very time when the mind of the natural philosopher, stirred by the great events of the Renaissance, was still under the spell of the Columbus discovery. Tycho Brahe and Kepler listened to Copernicus, because his words appealed to all who had heard the wonderful story of the bold sailor of Genoa. They listened, observed, and calculated, and they soon revealed the full meaning of the message which Copernicus gave to the world in his *De Revolutionibus Orbium Coelestium*. Brahe's observations and measurements and Kepler's calculations transformed the Copernican scheme into a physical reality, embodied in Kepler's laws of planetary motions. This was a triumph in which Brahe and Kepler had each an equal share with Copernicus, a share which assigned to each one of them a seat of honor in the Valhalla of Science.

The most precious part of this triumph was the great dynamical problem which it suggested, and which can be stated in the form of the question: Why do the planets move in accordance with Kepler's laws? This question was a hopeless puzzle to the science of the sixteenth century. But it was addressed to the inquiring mind of Europe when William Gilbert, Shakespeare's contemporary, was publishing his remarkable researches on electrical and magnetic forces; when Harvey had just startled the world by his discovery of the circulation of the blood; when Lord Francis

Bacon, thrilled by the great achievements of the inductive method of inquiry practiced by his scientific contemporaries, was composing the *Novum Organum;* and when young Galileo had just caught the startling message of Copernicus, Brahe, and Kepler. This exuberant intellectual activity of Europe could be expected to search for an answer to that perplexing question. Galileo was the first to approach it, when in the Cathedral of Pisa he had observed the isochronism of the swinging lamp. This observation suggested his historical experiments with freely falling bodies and with bodies gliding along inclined planes, which resulted in his discovery of the uniformly accelerated motions of freely falling bodies. Referring to this discovery great Lagrange said:

"It required an extraordinary genius to unravel laws of nature from phenomena which were always before our eyes but the understanding of which had escaped philosophical inquiry."

Lagrange referred not only to Galileo's ideally simple description of the motion of freely falling bodies, but also to the new physical concept which that description revealed. It was the concept of acceleration and of its relation to the moving force, so well expressed in Galileo's law of inertia known today as Newton's first law of motion. Pressure, weight, and tension were the only concepts asso-

ciated in those days with the idea of force.
Galileo's experiments were the first to reveal that
uniformly accelerated motion results from the
moving force which bodies experience when their
weight is not balanced by the counter pressure of
their supports. Acceleration became thus the new
concept associated with our ideas of force.

The problems of pendulum motions and of the
motions of projectiles yielded to Galileo, but his
dynamical science could not answer the question:
Why do the planets move in accordance with
Kepler's laws? Neither could the dynamical
science of Galileo's successors who preceded Newton answer it. Huyghens, Hooke, and Wren,
could not have answered it even if, as some of
them claimed, they had known Newton's law of
gravitational action. That answer was reserved
for Newton's laws of motion and his bold assumption that gravitational action obeys these laws.

Newton's predecessors failed to recognize that
the mass of material bodies is the most important
element in the circumstances which determine
their motions; that it is the determining factor in
their power of action and reaction. One of these
powers Newton detected in the momentum of the
moving mass; the other, the power of gravitational
action, he recognized as an inherent attribute of
every mass particle in the universe. The first he

expressed in terms of the actions and reactions which accompany the change of momenta; the other he expressed in terms of the attracting force as defined by his law of gravitational action. These were the forces which guided the motions in Galileo's experiments and in the impact experiments of Huyghens, Wallis, and of Newton himself. Guided by the light of these experiments Newton discovered the simplest measure of the actions and reactions exhibited by them. It was the time rate of change of momenta.

The momentum concept was created by Newton, and it is the most fundamental concept in his dynamics. His second law of motion expresses this fundamental character of the momentum concept by making its time rate of variation equal to the moving force. This measure of the acting and reacting forces not only conformed with the results of Galileo's experiments but, moreover, it shed a new light upon them which was not visible to Galileo nor to any of Newton's predecessors. It also agreed with all impact experiments, particularly with their revelation that during the impact of elastic bodies no momentum is lost.

The analysis of these impact experiments in the light of the second law was very helpful in the formulation of the third law, the law of equality of actions and reactions. Newton's third law employs a terminology the importance of which cannot be overstated. It demands that among the circumstances which determine the motion of a material system we must consider separately the forces impressed upon the system and the reactions of the system. This was never fully appreciated by Newton's predecessors, but I venture to say that this differentiation between the impressed and the reacting forces furnished an inestimable aid to our understanding of the energy principle. It was the experimental study of the reactions of materials which made the application of Newton's dynamics to physics and engineering a most powerful aid in their advancement.

The experimental basis which Newton inherited from his predecessors and which furnished the earliest support of his three laws of motion was neither deep nor broad, and Newton resorted to his rare intuition in the formulation of his laws. That intuition was never exhibited more strikingly than when Newton made the bold assumption that every mass particle in the universe obeyed the same law of gravitational action, and that the force by which this action manifests itself obeyed his laws of motion. Newton's intuition was guided by the great question of the sixteenth century science, the question, namely: Why do planets move in accordance with Kepler's laws?

Newton found the answer which said: The planets move in accordance with Kepler's description, because their motion is guided by Newton's gravitational forces which obey Newton's laws of motion.

Astronomical evidences supported Newton's answer and this assured the world that a new science, the science of dynamics, was born, and that Newton, inspired by Galileo, was its father. To this new science Newton added his great invention of a new mathematical art, the art of the differential and integral calculus. Laplace, one of the most ardent admirers of Newton's great achievements, declared that they would banish all empiricism from astronomy transforming it into a mathematical science. Halley, the greatest astronomer of Newton's time and a personal friend of Newton, is quoted by Voltaire as saying: "It will never be permitted to any mortal to approach nearer to Divinity."

Astronomy was during the eighteenth century the greatest expounder of the new physical reality, the reality of matter in motion, revealed by Newton's immortal essay: *Philosophiae Naturalis Principia Mathematica*. Other sciences, following the example of astronomy, began to feel the invigorating influence of Newton's philosophy. The foremost among them was the electrical science, which, two years after Newton's death, began to reveal a new physical reality, the reality of electricity in motion. Gray's discovery of electrical conductors; Franklin's demonstration that lightning is motion of electricity; Volta's discovery of a new source of electrical force; Oersted's discovery of the magnetic forces, produced by the motion of electricity; Faraday's discovery of electrical forces produced by varying magnetic forces—all these great achievements had prepared a splendid experimental foundation for a physical theory of electrical motions. The time was ripe for a new genius to formulate the fundamental laws which guide moving electricity just as Newton had formulated them for matter in motion. That genius was James Clerk Maxwell, an alumnus of Trinity College, the alma mater of immortal Newton. Maxwell's essay, *Dynamical Theory of the Electromagnetic Field*, occupies today a place of honor by the side of Newton's immortal essay. His electro-dynamics both in its form and in its fundamental concepts is an offspring of Newton's dynamics; hence it exhibits that remarkable similarity between matter in motion and electricity in motion. Newton's fundamental concept, the momentum, is Maxwell's fundamental concept; it is the electrokinetic momentum.

When Maxwell's dynamics prophesied the existence of electrical radiation and predicted that all radiation of visible and invisible light is probably electrical radiation, his language was not the vague language of a Delphic oracle. It was the clear language which he had learned from Newton. Newton and Maxwell blazoned the path to that high level of knowledge from which we are making today a new survey of the physical universe. In this survey electrical radiation enables us to catch a glimpse of a new meaning of the Newtonian concepts *mass* and *momentum*, and we are encouraged in the belief that this deeper meaning will be expressible in terms of the Newtonian actions and reactions of the electron and its field. This belief inspires the hope that a new dynamical science will soon be born, and that, like Maxwell's dynamics, it will be another daughter of Newton's dynamics. Some day, we hope, we shall be able to salute this new offspring of the Newtonian philosophy with the words of the Latin poet: *O matre pulchra filia pulchrior!*

NEWTON AS AN EXPERIMENTAL PHILOSOPHER

NEWTON AS AN EXPERIMENTAL PHILOSOPHER[1]

PAUL R. HEYL, Ph.D.

Physicist, United States Bureau of Standards, Washington

THE child is father to the man; fortunate is that child whose parents have the vision to recognize his early bent and the wisdom to encourage him to follow it.

Had Newton's elders lacked these qualities he would likely have become a small farmer as his father was before him, perhaps to be regarded by his neighbors as a visionary, or "a little queer;" but the fates were kind to him, and through him to us who follow him. Had it not been for the sympathetic interest of Newton's relatives, he who has been called "the greatest genius of the human race" might have lived and died without adequate opportunity for development and expression.

Natural inclinations sometimes reveal themselves very early in life, but only to those who have eyes to see. Maxwell showed his bent almost before he could talk plainly. Newton as a boy spent much time (which his schoolmaster doubtless

---

[1] Publication approved by the Director of the Bureau of Standards of the United States Department of Commerce.

thought might have been better employed) in the construction of kites and other mechanical toys. He made friends of the little girls of his acquaintance by making for them doll-furniture and such-like trinkets. As nobody in those days gave boys watches for birthday or Christmas presents he erected sun dials everywhere about the house and grounds. He built water mills and windmills, waterclocks and mechanical velocipedes.

Had this been all he might have escaped being a farmer only to be apprenticed to a cabinet maker; but he showed a bookish inclination that settled his fate, and to Cambridge he went, where his uncle had gone before him. Here he found congenial soil and a fostering atmosphere.

Of how he occupied his time as an undergraduate we have little record, but that little is significant. It is known that he devoted attention to the art of grinding lenses and to the theoretical principles of refraction, thus exhibiting from the start that happy combination of practice and theory which was characteristic of all his later work.

Soon we find him turning for a time from optics to chemistry, or rather to alchemy. Shortly after taking his degree he bought chemicals and a furnace, and seems to have spent some time with a relative in search for the philosopher's tincture. But fortunately for the progress of science he was recalled into the strait and narrow path by his appointment as professor of mathematics at Cambridge. It thus became his duty to lecture once a week on some subject with at least a mathematical connection, and he returned to his old love—optics.

Newton turned his acquired skill in the making of lenses to what was then the new art of grinding and polishing reflectors for telescopes. So skilful did he become in the construction of such reflectors that the best London opticians could not equal those of his production.

Newton's skill with his hands was in part innate, yet we must recognize that his superiority over the professional opticians of his time was doubtless due to the same cause that contributed to the excellence of the work of a certain painter, who when asked the secret of how he mixed his colors replied: "With brains, sir!" Newton's knowledge of geometry guided his technique, and furnished suggestions which could not have been expected to occur to the mind of the artisan of those days. Newton's methods, from the completeness with which he thought it worth while to describe them, must have differed greatly from the current practice of the lens-grinders of his day. The delicate finesse, original with him, can best be appreciated by reading his own detailed description and the evidence of his skill still survives in the reflecting telescope made by him and presented to the Royal Society.

Another instance of Newton's practical skill in laboratory arts is found in a description which he gives of an attempt to synthesize white light by mixing powders of the different tints of the spec trum. After producing a mixture which seemed good to him he fortunately found an opportunity of checking this opinion by that of an unprejudiced observer. While he had this powder spread out in the sunshine on the floor of his room with a piece of white paper lying beside it, a visitor came to his door. Newton stopped him from entering and asked him which of the two he considered the better white. After some hesitation the visitor confessed his inability to distinguish between them.

It is probable that the "white" paper of Newton's time would be considered distinctly off-color today. Such samples of old paper as have come down to us prove nothing one way or the other because of the effects of age; but Newton says of his powder that it was of the color of flesh, or newly cut wood. Even so, the production of such an approximation to white by mixing powders is not as easy as it looks.

But while we are at the door of Newton's room let us see what facilities he had for work. There

were no college laboratories in those days. The professor worked in his living room or in any place that came handy. Experimental work was so unusual that nobody thought of making provision for it. In all the faculty of the University of Cambridge Newton was, as far as we know, the only one addicted to this eccentric practice. Looking through his doorway we might have seen a small study such as may be found today in a few of the older buildings of the University; the window closed by a shutter with several holes in it, a desk littered with papers and lighted by a sputtering candle; a little dog with a diamond shaped mark near his tail, disporting himself in dangerous promimity to both candle and papers; a few prisms and lenses; a patch of white powder on the floor; a furnace in one corner; and then the man himself, as Alfred Noyes pictures him:

> "Obscure, unknown, the shadow of a man
> In darkness, like a grey dishevelled ghost,
> Bare throated, down at heel, his last night's supper
> Littering his desk, untouched; his glimmering face
> Under his tangled hair, intent and still,
> Preparing our new universe."

In the *Principia* as well as in the *Opticks* there is to be found evidence of Newton's skill of hand and experimental ingenuity. Perhaps the most noteworthy is his experiment to test whether the acceleration of gravity is the same for all bodies.

He recognized that experiments with falling bodies could give but rough results. For greater accuracy he set up two pendulums, equally long, whose bobs were composed of what we would call today two wooden "pill boxes" of equal size. He filled one of these, he says, "with wood," and put an equal weight of gold in the other, placing it as accurately as he could so that its center of oscillation should correspond with that of the other pendulum; a difficult adjustment, and one upon which the validity of the result closely depends. His skill of hand and eye is evidenced by the fact that the two pendulums when set in motion differed in time of swing by less than one part in a thousand.

Even the members of the Royal Society, a body of men selected for their excellence in scientific knowledge and attainments and, as the minutes of their meetings show, assiduous experimenters, bore testimony to Newton's experimental skill. Newton had transmitted to them an account of an electrical experiment which they had tried to repeat without success, and were forced to write to him for farther instruction as to the method of carrying it out. Newton in his reply comments on the difficulty of the experiment, and gives details of the finesse, the "tapping with the fingers" necessary for success.

And yet I think that Newton would have been

rather surprised had he heard himself described as an "experimental" philosopher, and would have considered the expression tautological. The scientific specialization of our time was unknown to him. The term philosopher meant then what its etymology signifies—a lover of wisdom, and wisdom (it was beginning to be recognized) was to be found by questioning Nature by experiment. In our day the results of experiment have reached such proportions and exhibit such complexity that there is a legitimate place for what is called the "theoretical man," who studies and interprets these results, viewed with a detachment and a perspective that the experimentalist, with his eyes close to his work, cannot always attain. But in Newton's time experiment was still in its infancy. The philosopher had to dig for his own material upon which to philosophize, and Newton did both. He swung his pendulums, and he mused under the apple tree; he ground and mixed his pigments, and speculated on the nature of light; for him experiment and theory were inseparable.

This state of affairs was a reaction from the mental attitude of the Middle Ages, when all philosophic thought was deductive, when men spun explanations of natural phenomena out of their own inner consciousness, unguided by experiment, and sorry tangles they often made of it. The

intellectuals of mediaeval times were pure theorists. Experiment was even frowned upon.   Roger Bacon, a man centuries before his time, incurred the suspicion of witchcraft, though in holy orders, because he experimented and observed the heavenly bodies. The similar fate of Galileo is well known.   Francis Bacon, a leader in the intellectual revolt, and a notable champion of induction and experiment is perhaps seldom regarded as a practical experimenter, but it is to be remembered that he came to his death by illness contracted in a personally conducted experiment on cold storage of meat.   From his day onward the experimental philosopher has been of increasing importance.

In modern times even such a pure theorist as Einstein staked the success or failure of his startling hypotheses upon the results of three experimental tests, all of which have now been successfully completed.   And when we think of Newton as Noyes calls him, "the king of thought," let us also bear in mind that upon which his thought was founded and without which thought is as barren as faith without works—painstaking, careful experiment.

DEVELOPMENTS FOLLOWING FROM NEWTON'S WORK

DEVELOPMENTS FOLLOWING FROM NEWTON'S WORK

ERNEST W. BROWN, M.A. (CANTAB.), Sc.D.

Professor of Mathematics in Yale University

WHILE the title of this essay permits a wide degree of freedom in the subject matter, I shall confine myself mainly to those aspects of the developments of Newton's laws of motion and of gravitation which have lain in my own particular field of work, namely, the motions of individual bodies resulting from the applications of these laws. An attempt to take a wider range would involve me in descriptions which touch so many sides of our modern daily life that there would be no opportunity to get down to those details which are necessary if a concrete idea is to be given of the applications to the moon and planets.

And yet I cannot altogether leave them aside because there is no essential difference between the manner in which we apply Newton's laws to the motion of a heavenly body and that which is used to study the behavior of a man-made machine. The structure of a "skyscraper," the safety of a railway bridge, the motion of the motor car, the flight of an airplane, the navigation of a ship across the ocean, the measure of time itself, depend fundamentally on correct applications of Newton's laws of motion. It is true that much more is needed by the engineer than a knowledge of these laws, but I believe that it is equally true that we may trace many failures of our mechanical devices, especially of those which move at high speed, to lack of knowledge or lack of care in applying the laws. It is unfortunate that there has been a tendency to substitute for thorough study of the foundations of mechanics and of the methods by which they are developed, the current applications in the form of rules of procedure. This tendency, which the rapid development of material resources has perhaps assisted, is likely to become expensive and to delay future development if it is not checked. The real difficulty involved is the somewhat extensive training in mathematics which is necessary; few are both willing and able to obtain this training owing to the small demand for their services. The practical need for fundamental researches in the mechanics of motion is, however, becoming increasingly necessary, and I believe the day is not far distant when manufacturers of moving machinery will demand the presence of such men, just as in other lines the services of highly trained chemists and physicists are already utilized. Research in the so-called pure science of mechanics, that is, research in which the motive is not the application to practical needs but simply the search for knowledge, is as necessary here as it is in other fields of endeavor, because the experience of the past has shown that this is the main path to progress.

If one is asked to describe in a sentence the chief service which Newton rendered to mankind, the question may perhaps be best answered by saying that he taught how to predict the future. The statement is of course applicable to nearly all fundamental research. It is true that in many cases we still see "through a glass darkly," but the chance of success in predicting with even limited knowledge to that without it, has been too often illustrated to need further stress. In certain of the applications of the laws of motion and gravitation to astronomy, the success in prediction has been so great that it has amounted to what would ordinarily be termed practical certainty. It is indeed a remarkable feat to be able to predict successfully within a second of time the moment when the moon or a planet will be observed due south a century hence. In the ordinary routine of the astronomer it is regularly done even more accurately, five years ahead, and the leeway necessary when the interval is extended is known. It should be added that such allowance as is made for errors is mainly due not to defects in the laws themselves but to other causes on which I shall touch briefly later.

Isaac Newton not only laid down the laws but shared with Leibnitz the honor of furnishing the chief instrument by means of which the consequences of those laws have been worked out. We should indeed be almost helpless, in the face of the great complexities which the laws produce, without the assistance of the calculus—the method of fluxions or rates as Newton called it. But I should be doing its founders far less than justice in presenting it merely as a tool for the study of gravitation and mechanics, widely as it has entered into all subjects where rates of change have to be considered. It is in fact one of the foundation stones on which that great structure of thought which we know as pure mathematics has been built.

In order to predict the position of any heavenly body we need two main elements. One, a knowledge of the laws by which its motion is guided, was furnished by Newton. The second, a knowledge of its position and velocity at any one moment in the past, is furnished by the observer. In order to be able to tell when and where a shell fired from a gun will hit, it is necessary to know the position of the gun, the velocity of the shell when it leaves the gun, and the moment of firing, as well as the laws which govern its flight. It will serve just as well if we know the position and velocity at any moment during its flight. Similar information must be available for a heavenly body. But the observer, his telescope, and his clock are all fallible, and he can only hope to secure accuracy by continually repeating his observations and comparing them with the predictions. Every careful observation contributes something towards increased accuracy. In the two centuries since Newton's time, some one hundred thousand observations of the sun and moon alone have been utilized to secure the initial data which are now used to predict the future positions of those bodies. Besides these, there have been many hundreds of thousands of observations of stars made to regulate the clock, which is of equal importance with the telescope in securing the necessary information. Further, while it may take only a few minutes to prepare for and secure a single observation, by the time that the observation has been fully utilized these few minutes have stretched to hours, so that the time and labor ultimately spent in gathering the needed material from observation have become very great.

These are, so to speak, the specifications on which detailed plans for the motion of each body are to be made out, the plan, or what is called the theory, being then constructed according to Newton's laws by the mathematician. Properly they are needed with high accuracy at the outset. But since the only way to correct the errors of the specifications is by comparison with the theory, the latter must be at least partially constructed at the outset with not very accurate specifications. Thus there is a double process continually in operation. A theory is constructed by means of which the future position of the body can be roughly predicted. The prediction is compared with observation, and when enough comparisons have been made the specifications can be corrected and the theory altered to fit the corrections. As the comparisons become more numerous the theory must be worked out with greater accuracy. But the labor of working out the theory increases rapidly with the degree of accuracy demanded, so that in our own time with centuries of observations behind us, it is no small task to carry out the work.

There has, in fact, been a continual contest between the observer and the mathematician some what like that between the makers of guns and armor plate, with this difference, however, that every shell which is fired from the gun can be used to strengthen the armor to resist future shells. It has to be confessed that up to the last quarter of a century the observer has had the best of the contest, partly perhaps because he had an earlier start, and partly because his tools in the early stages were easier to handle. At the present time honors seem to be about even. In some cases the observer can obtain the place of the body more accurately than it can be predicted; in others, the reverse is the case. However, the friendly contest conducted in a coöperative spirit has at last brought us to the stage where we can not only detect the variations from complete accuracy of the laws themselves but also the irregularities of the clock by means of which time is measured, namely, the earth in its daily motion round its axis.

Newton himself only carried the developments from his laws sufficiently far so as to make quite rough tests of their sufficiency to explain the motions of the bodies in the solar system. While the methods which he actually used for investigation were probably the same in principle as those now adopted, he set them forth in his great work, the *Principia*, in a manner which, while it served his immediate purposes, had somewhat far-reaching effects. In his time the methods of proof generally supposed to be rigorous were geometrical. If he had used his new method of fluxions, it would have been necessary for his contemporaries first to master the method and then its applications. Whether it was from a desire to avoid controversy or from a wish to have immediate acceptance of his work, or perhaps both, he cast all his proofs into a geometrical form. This itself was a *tour de force* exhibiting perhaps as great ability as that by which the laws themselves were proved. He had his reward. Few scientific men have had their theories so quickly accepted or have been held in such honor during their lifetime not only at home but also abroad. In England, the respect for his authority was so great that for nearly a century and a half not only his work but his published methods were considered to be fundamental. As a consequence, little progress was made, chiefly because the geometrical method itself is not capable of great expansion where numerical calculations have to be made. Respect for authority was doing the same harm to progress in England as it had during the middle ages in the rest of Europe. We now know that the authority of even the greatest investigator should begin to wane as soon as he stops work. His successors build on what he has done and it is of the essence of progress that they should build better with increased knowledge and newer tools. Invocation of past authority is the chief weapon of the reactionary. The results attained may stand for all time, but the methods of attack to secure new territory will have to change with changing conditions and new problems.

On the continent one investigator after another took up Newton's work. But they applied all the resources which were being furnished by the development of mathematical methods, and in fact stimulated to so great an extent the search for new methods that it may be said with some justice that the progress of pure mathematics during the eighteenth century was largely due to the effort to develop the consequences of Newton's laws of motion and gravitation. The great challenge was the problem set by the moon. As our nearest neighbor, its deviations from simple elliptic motion were more easily observed than those of any of the planets, and it had long been known that the deviations themselves were relatively greater. Newton himself had been able to show that the theory could roughly account for most of the larger deviations and it was hoped that, by extending the calculations, all of the motions which had been observed could be deduced from the theory. Amongst these investigators, L. A. Euler, a Swiss who spent most of his life in Russia, stands out, in my opinion, as the greatest. The initial stages of every method which has had any success since his time are to be found in his published works. His fertility and industry have rarely been exceeded and his activities did not stop when he became totally blind.

A great impetus was given to the whole subject at the beginning of the nineteenth century by the publication of the Mécanique Céleste. In this great treatise Laplace not only placed the mathematical treatment on a firmer foundation, discovering in the process various remarkable consequences of the laws of gravitation, but showed how, by industry and perserverance, the work of calculating the effects of the law could be carried to any degree of accuracy desired. At least, it was so thought for a century; we now know that there is a limit to the possible accuracy of these methods although, as far as comparison with observation is concerned, this limit is very far from being reached. The response soon came. One worker after another devoted a large fraction of his life to the developments, each trying to surpass his predecessor in the accuracy and extent of his work. By the middle of the century, theory seemed to have caught up with observation. Leverrier for the planets and Hansen for the moon appeared to have completed the task begun by Newton two centuries earlier.

When this stage had been reached a complete survey was possible. The numerous observations which had been accumulating in many observatories could be compared with theory and the sufficiency of the laws tested. The first great result of this comparison was the prediction by Adams and Leverrier of the existence of the planet Neptune, hitherto unseen, by means of its gravitational effect on Uranus. Then Adams threw a bomb-shell into the camp by showing that the known slow approach of the moon to the earth could not be fully accounted for by gravitation alone, as Laplace had thought; the new theoretical calculation gave only half the necessary amount. A hot controversy raged for several years as to the correctness of Adams' work, and in this battle nearly every theorist fought. One after another, each using his own weapons, came round to Adams' result. Out of this arose with gradually increasing certainty, our present knowledge that tidal friction is very slowly bringing the moon nearer the earth, and at the same time gradually lengthening the day.

This work of Adams has greatly stimulated research. Not only has it been necessary to carry the theories of the moon and planets further, so as to obtain greater accuracy, but every possible help has had to be derived from observation. At one end, eclipses doubtfully recorded more than three thousand years ago have been utilized: at the other, observations of the tides and currents in the Behring Sea have been pressed into service. In the one case, gravitational theory had to be able to say whether an eclipse of the sun was total at a given spot on the earth's surface thousands of years ago; in the other, the mechanism by which tidal friction slowed down the earth had to be studied in order to calculate its amount. The whole story is a fascinating chapter in scientific history, but I must press on to other matters.

In this and many other ways the laws of Newton have been put to the proof. We have now reached a position where we can begin to distinguish more clearly between lack of accuracy in the statement of the laws themselves, insufficiency of our theoretical developments from them, and want of precision in the observations made to test them. As to the first, you have heard in previous papers the new statement of the laws which is now included in the general term "the theory of relativity" and I shall not make further reference to it except for a single remark from the point of view of one whose efforts have been mainly directed towards developing the consequences of Newton's laws and comparing them with observation. The structure has been built up on what we thought was bed rock. It seems very probable now that it is not so. The base is still an enormous block fully capable of carrying the superstructure, but it is now seen to rest on deeper foundations. Since this discovery was made, all that has been necessary to make the block firm has been the insertion of two or three very small wedges. The change, in fact, is rather in the description given of the foundations themselves.

Nothing in astronomy that I know of which has depended on observation and calculation has had to be rejected with the new views; a new interpretation only to certain portions of the record has been given. The theoretical developments for the moon and major planets are now temporarily waiting until further observations shall show need for improvements, but work on the smaller bodies is going forward—somewhat slowly it is true, for it is difficult and the laborers are few. New methods for increasing the precision of the observations seem to be required: we are still mainly using the methods of the past two centuries with the improvements resulting from better construction and greater care.

All the earlier work was directed towards the motion of bodies within the solar system. As observations of the stars accumulated there were found many pairs which appeared to revolve round one another: did they do so under the Newtonian laws? The answer has been in the affirmative within the errors of observation. Perhaps it would be more correct to say that we have no reason to believe that the laws under which matter moves in stellar systems are different from those which hold in the solar system. Investigations into the gravitational possibilities of stellar systems containing more than two masses have scarcely begun. I

[123]

have pointed out elsewhere that we know examples of only two types of motion of three bodies, and both of these fortunately are types which can be dealt with by well-known methods. Stellar systems belong to the type in which two of the bodies are near to each other compared with their distance from the third body: their effects on one another are dealt with by a slight modification of the lunar theory.

The telescope has, however, revealed assemblages of thousands of stars which exhibit a certain degree of regularity. Globular clusters and spiral nebulae owe their peculiar forms mainly, I believe, to the effects of gravitation; very little is yet known as to the way in which these effects are produced. The problem at the outset is one for the mathematician to attack. Newton's name runs no danger of being forgotten when his work is subjected to the acid test for all scientific work, namely, its capacity for further development.

NEWTON'S TWENTY YEARS' DELAY IN ANNOUNCING THE LAW OF GRAVITATION

NEWTON'S TWENTY YEARS' DELAY IN ANNOUNCING THE LAW OF GRAVITATION

FLORIAN CAJORI, Ph.D.

Professor of the History of Mathematics, University of California

IT IS well known that Newton in 1665 or 1666 first tested the law of universal gravitation, but that he did not announce the law until 1686. Before the year 1887, it was universally accepted that Newton's delay of about twenty years in announcing this great law was due to his having used in 1665 or 1666 too small a value for the size of the earth so that, in applying his gravitational hypothesis to the earth's attraction for the moon, he obtained a theoretical result for the distance a body falls from rest on the surface of the earth in one second which did not agree with experiment, and that he could not get the two results to agree until the Frenchman J. Picard supplied a more accurate geodetic determination for the size of the earth.

At the two hundredth anniversary of the publication of Newton's *Principia*, in 1887, the astronomer J. C. Adams and the mathematician J. W. L. Glaisher advanced another explanation of the twenty-year delay. They stated that in 1666 fairly accurate values of the earth's radius were known and that the real cause of the delay was the question how a sphere attracts an outside particle. This question Newton did not clear up until sometime in 1685, and not until then did be consider valid his proof of the law of gravitation, as applied to the earth and moon.

Present disagreement. Adams and Glaisher did not enter into the examination of all the minute historical details which arise in the endeavor to decide which of the two explanations of the twenty years' delay is valid. Of the two explanations neither was definitely proved by them to be true or to be false. The full text of Glaisher's address was published in the *Cambridge Chronicle* of April 20, 1888, a local publication not accessible to readers at large. In consequence astronomers and historians of the present time are divided on this question. The preponderance of opinion apparently favors the old explanation as voiced by the poet Alfred Noyes in his "Watchers of the Sky:"

> ". . . . . Newton withheld his hope
> Until that day when light was brought from France,
> New light, new hope, in one small glistening fact,
> Clear-cut as any diamond; and to him
> Loaded with all significance, like the point
> Of light that shows where constellations burn.
> Picard in France—all glory to her name
> Who is herself a light among all lands—
> Had measured earth's diameter once more

[128]

With exquisite precision. To the throng,
Those few corrected ciphers, his results,
Were less than nothing; yet they changed the world.
For Newton seized them and, with trembling hands,
Began to work his problem out anew.
Then, then, as on the page those figures turned
To hieroglyphs of heaven, and he beheld
The moving moon, with awful cadences
Falling into the path his law ordained,
Even to the foot and second, his hand shook
And dropped the pencil. 'Work it out for me,'
He cried to those around him; for the weight
Of that celestial music overwhelmed him;"

The Italian historian of mathematics, Gino Loria,[1] in a delightful sketch of the life of Newton, says that Newton abandoned his theory "because of certain irreconcilable contradictions to which he was led by the application of an imperfect measure of the diameter of the earth" and that later, "having information of the more precise congenerous result obtained by Picard in France, he resumed anew those genial studies." Loria repeats the story or the legend that in going over the calculation with the new data, Newton was taken with such intense emotion,[2] that he had to secure the assistance of a friend. The noted German

[1] G. Loria, *Newton*, Roma, 1920, p. 21.

[2] "There does not appear to be any contemporary authority for these particulars," says S. P. Rigaud in his *First Publication of Sir Isaac Newton's Principia*, Oxford, 1838, p. 6. Rigaud first finds the story in Dr. Robison's *Mechanical Philosophy*, 1804, p. 288, and Vol. II, 1822, p. 94.

[129]

historian of science, Friedrich Dannemann,[3] and the English physicist, H. Buckley[4] refer to Newton's failure in 1666, as due to his use of only sixty miles to a degree of latitude.

In a recent school history of science[5] we read that in 1666 Newton "laid all his papers aside in the belief that he was wrong" and that "about 17 years later he heard that a new measurement of the diameter of the earth had been made" and he repeated the calculation which "convinced him that his idea had been correct." Another recent historian of science[6] dwells upon Newton's dilemma in 1666: "By a tragedy of misfortune for which Newton was not to blame, his test was doomed at first to disappointment. The accuracy of the result depended upon the accuracy of the value taken as the radius of the earth. Newton could only take the accepted value of the times, and it was, alas, wrong. It was assumed to be 3436 miles, whereas the correct value is 3963 miles." A recent French-Swiss writer, Arnold Reymond,[7] speaking of the meridian measurement of the Greek

[3] F. Dannemann, *Die Naturwissenschaften in ihrer Entwickelung*, Vol. 2, second edition Leipzig, 1921, pp. 20, 21.

[4] H. Buckley, *A Short History of Physics*, London, 1927, p. 34.

[5] J. A Cochrane, *A School History of Science*, London, 1925, p. 60.

[6] Ivor B. Hart, *Makers of Science*, London, 1923.

[7] A. Reymond, *History of the Sciences in Greco-Roman Antiquity*, translation by R. G. de Bray, New York, 1927, p. 83.

Eratosthenes, exclaims: "Had Newton been acquainted with it, he would have been able to verify his hypothesis of gravitation, without being obliged to shelve it for years until Picard succeeded in measuring the radius of the earth more exactly." Similarly, we read in a leading article on Newton, in the London *Times* Literary Supplement for March 17, 1927, that when Newton was twenty-three years of age, "he was hampered in his calculations by having assumed an incorrect value for the radius of the earth." The same view is taken by S. Brodetsky in his recent life of Newton.[8] According to the astronomer-royal of England, Sir Frank Dyson,[9] "it is said, but without much evidence, that Newton used the erroneous value 60 miles for 1° of latitude of the earth's surface;" yet Dyson concludes that Newton "obtained a value one-seventh part too small, and in view of this discrepancy for a time turned his thoughts to other things." The article "Newton" in the eleventh edition of the *Encyclopaedia Britannica* makes no reference to the views of Adams and Glaisher.

On the other hand, R. T. Glazebrook in his article "Newton" in the *Dictionary of National Biography*, and the Oxford astronomer H. H. Turner

[8] S. Brodetsky, *Sir Isaac Newton*, London, 1927, pp. 50, 52, 88, 89.

[9] Sir Frank Dyson, *Nature*, Supplement: The Newton Celebration, Vol. 119, March 26, 1927, p. 30.

in an article in the London *Times* of March 19, 1927, strongly support the history of the discovery of gravitation as set forth by Adams and Glaisher in 1888. Turner supplies details which we shall reproduce later. In Belgium, B. Lefebvre[10] and in Germany H. Wieleitner[11] presented the view of Adams and Glaisher in articles on Newton and the law of gravitation.

Aim of this article. It is the purpose of this paper to make a searching study of what was really known in England respecting the size of the earth, before Picard made his measurements, and to subject the entire question of Newton's delay to a critical examination.

BRITISH VIEWS OF THE SIZE OF THE EARTH BEFORE 1671

We pass in exhaustive review opinions and measurements on the size of the earth found in early British authors, and in translations of foreign works into English. It will appear that the early British mile was usually the same as the Roman mile of 5000 feet, the Roman foot being somewhat shorter than the present English foot.[12] The

---

[10] B. Lefebvre, *Revue des Questions scientifiques*, juillet, 1924, et janvier 1925.

[11] H. Wieleitner, *Unterrichtsblätter für Math. u. Naturw.*, Vol. 33, 1927, p. 103.

[12] A. DeMorgan, *Companion to the British Almanac*, 1836, p. 35. According to the *Century Dictionary* under "Mile," English writers of the sixteenth century often call 625 feet a furlong, and the reason is that 5 feet was taken to be a

English statute mile [we shall abbreviate "Eng. st. mi."] was introduced later, it being, perhaps undesignedly on the part of the framers, defined by an act passed in the thirty-fifth year of the reign of Elizabeth [1593] to be "8 furlongs of 40 perches of 16½ ft. each," that is 5280 feet. By this act persons were forbidden to build within three miles of London. Whether this mile had become common and only needed the sanction of law, or whether it was a new measure, cannot be gathered.[13] We begin our account with Robert Hues.

Robert Hues' Tractatus de Globis appeared at London in 1592[14] and an English translation in 1633 and 1659. Hues was a graduate of Oxford, a Greek scholar, and gave a whole chapter of his book to an examination of Greek and other writings relating to the size of the earth. Hues[15] expresses all lengths in terms of "furlongs" which are used for the ancient "stadia." He says that Aristotle's assertion in the second book of his *De Coelo*, that the circumference of the earth is 400,000 furlongs (or 1° = 123.2 Eng. st. mi.) "is only

---

pace, so that a Roman mile of 1000 paces would be 8×625 feet. In the *Encyclopaedia Britannica*, eleventh edition, "Weights and Measures," we read, p. 481, "The English foot has not appreciably varied in several centuries."

[13] A. De Morgan, article "Mile" in the *English Cyclopaedia*, London, 1867.

[14] Robert Hues, *Tractatus de Globis*, edited by C. R. Markham, London, 1889.

[15] Robert Hues, *Tractatus de Globis*, Third Part, Chapter 2, pp. 80–94.

defended by a great name." Hues is very critical
of Eratosthenes and Posidonius, because they
accepted reports of distances between cities without
actual measurement. He places greater confidence
in Ptolemy's figures. Hues takes 60 English miles
(of 5000 English feet) to a degree "which agrees
exactly with that of Ptolemy." At the end of
the chapter, Hues gives the following summary of
the data for a degree of latitude which "carry in
them any shew of probability:"

AUTHORS	FURLONGS	ENGLISH STATUE MILES
Strabo and Hipparchus..............................	700	79.55
Eratosthenes..	694¼	78.91
Posidonius and the ancient Arabians.................	666⅔	75.76
Ptolemy and our Englishmen........................	500	56.82
The later Arabian..................................	566⅔	64.39
Italians and Germans...............................	480	54.55

The second column represents our own translation
of Hues' results into English statute miles per degree
of latitude. Hues says: "In this so great diversity
of opinions concerning the true measure of the
earth's circumference, let it be free for every man to
follow whomsoever he please."

The Spanish authors Cortes and Medina. About the
middle of the sixteenth century two treatises on
systematic navigation appeared in Spain, one by
Pedro de Medina, the other by Martin Cortes.

These works were translated into French, Dutch and other languages. An English writer[16] on the history of navigation states that Richard Eden published a translation of Cortes at London in 1561, that "it underwent various impressions, whilst the English translation of Medina's work, though made within twenty years after the other, seems to have been neglected." We have seen a French translation of Medina, and an English translation of Cortes of the year 1596.[17] From Cortes we quote: "But to our purpose, let us giue to euery league three thousand pases, and to euery pase fiue foote, and so shall euery league have .XV. thousande foote. In the Cardes [charts] of the sea, that haue their degrees of .XV. leagues and two terces, we say: that of these, the roundnesse of the lande and the water conteineth six thousande leagues. And in the Cardes that haue seuenteene leagues and a halfe for a degree, of these we say that it conteyneth six thousande and three hundred leagues." From this and other passages in Cortes we gather that the "mile" contained 1000 "pases" (paces) or 5000 feet, that the league varied in different countries, that Spain counted a league

[16] James Wilson, "Dissertation on the Rise and Progress of the Modern Art of Navigation," in Maseres' *Scriptores Logarithmici*, Vol. 4, 1801, p. 321, republished from John Robertson's *Elements of Navigation*, thirteenth edition, 1772.

[17] *The Arte of Navigation . . . First written in Spanish by Martin Curtis, and translated into English by Richard Eden*, London, 1596, folio 15 B.

15,000 feet, and one degree of latitude 16⅔ or 17½ leagues, which is 50 or 50½ "miles" per degree. The second Spanish writer, Medina[18] gives precisely the same table of lengths, up to the "league" and then says that "17½ leagues make a degree." Thus Medina's degree measured 52½ "miles," where each mile contained 5000 feet of the kind defined by 64 grains of barley. If a Spanish mile was 1391.7 meters,[19] then the Spanish foot was about 11 English inches, and the 50 or 50½ "miles" per degree cited above, are equivalent to $1° = 43.24$ and 45.4 Eng. st. mi., the true value being about $1° = 69.1$ Eng. st. mi.

Edward Wright's summary of data. In 1610 Edward Wright published the second edition of his widely known work entitled *Certain Errors in Navigation detected and corrected* in which he says, regarding the earth's semidiameter,[20] "There is great variety of Opinions amongst the Ancient and later Writers, some making it to be almost 8000 miles; some little more than 5500, some others not much exceeding 5000; others making it lesse then 3600; and others not much more than 3200, as Alphraganus, though Fernelius, according to his

---

[18] Pierre de Medina, *L'Art de Naviguer . . . tradvict . . . par Nicolas de Nicolai*, Lyon, 1569, p. 78.

[19] L. J. Jackson, *Metrology*, London, 1882, p. 66.

[20] We are quoting from the third or 1657 edition of E. Wright's *Certain Errors in Navigation detected and corrected*, edited by Josph Moxon.

Observation, findes it to be 3900 miles, whereas others of late will have it little more than 3000." This passage is of interest, because it again strongly emphasizes the great diversity of values assigned to the earth's radius. The extremes are 8000 miles and 3000 miles! The further question arises, what kind of miles are these? Are they English statute miles or some other kind? Fernel's "3900 miles" should supply a key to this question. Now 3900 miles for the radius means 68.06 miles per degree of latitude. Richard Norwood[21] took those 68.06 miles to be "Italian miles" of 1000 paces each, and remarked "the pace which he Fernel used being more than five of our English feet." But in the "Dedicatory" of his book, Norwood admits that the Italian mile is commonly taken to be 5000 English feet. De Morgan accepted this last definition of the Italian mile.[22] Interpreting, then, the "miles" mentioned by Wright as miles containing 5000 English feet each, the "8000 miles" for the earth's radius, which is probably Aristotle's value in round numbers, is equivalent to $1° = 132.2$ Eng. st. mi. Wright's "3000 miles" yield $1° = 49.3$ Eng. st. mi.

Wright's edition of Zamorano (also "Samorano"). To Wright's *Certain Errors in Navigation* of 1610 and

[21] R. Norwood, *The Sea-Mans Practice*, London, 1662, p. 37.
[22] A. De Morgan, *Philosophical Magazine*, Vol. 19, 1841, p. 446.

1657 is appended a translation into English ("by a friend of mine") of Roderigo Samorano's Spanish book, the *Art of Navigation*, "which Treatise I would wish all them that are but New beginners in that Art first to peruse, and understand well before they come to the reading of the former which . . . . requireth such a one as is alreadie reasonably well acquainted with the rules and principles of the Art." Of interest to us is Samorano's 6300 Spanish leagues as a measure of the circumference of the earth, with the added statement (p. 5) that 1 league is 4000 paces and 1 pace is 5 feet. If this foot is the same as the English foot, then we get the very creditable value of $1° = 66.29$ Eng. st. mi. As we shall see, this is more than what Wright himself found from his geodetic measurement. Nevertheless, he nowhere urges the acceptance of his own value to that given by Samorano. After praising the Spanish book, Wright issues a warning, "I must admonish the reader" to use his own sea chart and not that of Samorano, but no similar warning is sounded regarding Samorano's value for the size of the earth.

Wright's determination of the earth's radius. This determination is seldom referred to by geodesists,[23]

[23] We have seen reference to it as being a matter of interest overlooked by geodesists, in an article by O. Zanotti-Bianco in *Atti della R. Accademia delle Science*, Vol. 19, Torino, 1883, p. 791, also in an article by M. F. Marguet in *Bulletin Astronomique*, Vol. 35, Paris, 1918, pp. 238–241.

even though his *Certain Errors in Navigation,* in the 1610 and 1657 editions which contain this determination is widely quoted. The reason is probably, that Wright himself admitted that his measurement was done under unsatisfactory conditions. He stated that to secure great accuracy, the length of all Great Britain, from north to south should be measured and the latitudes of the end points carefully determined. He had not the means to carry out such an extensive program. Nevertheless he wished to ascertain for himself, where between 8000 miles and 3000 miles, the true value lay, approximately. In the year 1589 he selected a hill near Plymouth sound and measured on the hill a base line of 664 feet ("so much as the ground would well give me leave to take, for otherwise I would have gone further"). He took this base as the side of a triangle whose third vertex was a small rock, below, at the sea water, and measured the two angles of that triangle at the extremities of the base line. He then calculated the distance from his station at one end of the base line on the hill, to the rock below. Next he measured the angular depression of that rock as seen from his station on the hill, and also the angular depression of the visible horizon. From these data he computed the earth's radius as 18,312,621 feet, which, we find, yields $1° = 60.54$

Eng. st. mi. As we shall see, this is the smallest value for the size of the earth which has been recorded as having been obtained by actual measurement. Wright states in his Preface that he used his value in finding the correction of the angular altitude of heavenly bodies as determined by the cross-staff at an elevation above sea-level. A small table of corrections is appended. If, for example, the observer is 20 feet above sea-level, then 3′ 35″ are to be subtracted from the observed angular altitude of a heavenly body. Both William Oughtred and Richard Norwood declared Wright's determination of the size of the earth as inadequate.

Conclusion. The outstanding result of our examination of Wright's publication is, (1) the emphasis upon the extreme diversity of the different estimates of the size of the earth, (2) his own measurement, based on data, the inadequacy of which he recognizes and admits, yielding $1° = 60.54$ Eng. st. mi., (3) the inclusion, in his book, of Samorano's treatise in which the data used in navigation are equivalent to $1° = 66.29$ Eng. st. mi.

Did Oughtred measure the earth? In his *Addition vnto the Vse of the Instrvment called the Circles of Proportion, For the Working of Nauticall Questions,* London, 1633, William Oughtred devotes part of a chapter to "finding the circuit of the earth in miles." Edward Wright's method did not appeal to him: "That way which is by the height of an hill, and a tangent line from thence to the superficies of the sea, is rather a phantasie, then a thing of actuall performance" (p. 21). An accurate determination should involve distances as great as London to Edinburgh, which would involve great expense. As a preliminary, he suggests a way, which may be practised by "any ingenious student, whose sight both of his eyes and understanding is quicke and perspicacious." Set up two poles, 528 feet apart, one west of the other. At a point A of the east pole adjust a level, and sight a point B on the west pole. Moving the level to the point B, and adjusting the level, sight a point C at the first pole, above A. Carefully measure AC. The right triangle ABC is similar to the right triangle ABX, where X is the center of the earth. The earth's radius AX is found by proportion. Oughtred does not say that he made this measurement. But he gives a numerical example, which yields 351,120 feet per degree, and he goes into so much minute detail as to the kind of a level to construct, the kind of day to select, observing at the east pole about eleven o'clock in the morning, and at the west pole about one o'clock, and making so many other suggestions, that the reader feels that Oughtred must have carried out the experiment himself. Oughtred mentions in his book both Wright and

[141]

Snell. Probably influenced by Snell, Oughtred takes "miles 66¼, that is 349,800 feete to answer to a degree upon the earth" (p. 27), but he says (p. 21) that it is "usually taken, or rather mistaken, that 60 such miles [English miles by statute] make a degree."

Issac Newton, as a boy, studied Oughtred's *Clavis mathematicae*, whether in 1666 he was familiar with the book of Oughtred from which we have quoted is not known. He quotes from it much later, in a letter of May 25, 1694, on a new course of study for Christ's Hospital.[24]

Norwood's Trigonometry. Richard Norwood wrote two books which demand our attention, his *Trigonometrie*, 1631, and his *Sea-Mans Practice*, 1636, both of which went through several editions. The former reached its fourth edition in 1661, the latter its seventh edition in 1667. The *Trigonometrie* gave much attention to the art of navigation. In this book[25] Norwood took 20 leagues per degree of latitude, and 3 leagues per mile; this means 60 miles per degree. The very great convenience of having 60 units of length to the degree of latitude, so that one minute of latitude would measure 1 unit of length, requires emphasis. We shall see that in

[24] J. Edleston, *Correspondence of Sir Isaac Newton and Professor Cotes*, London, 1850, pp. 279-292.

[25] R. Norwood, *Trigonometrie*, 1631, pp. 84, 102.

1635 Norwood measured 1° = 69.5 Eng. st. mi.; nevertheless in his books he continued to use 60 miles to the degree. In this procedure he was wise. For purposes of navigation it was more convenient to change the size of the mile, than to change the number of miles per degree. And so we find Norwood adhering to 60 mi. = 1°, but taking his mile to contain, not 5000 feet or 5280 feet, but 6120 feet. Later this procedure led to the definition of the nautical mile by the British Admiralty as 6080 feet—a practice which has been continued to modern times.

Norwood's historical summary. In his *Sea-Mans Practice,*[26] Norwood cites the Arabian astronomers of 827 A. D. and their measurement of the earth's degree in the fields of Mesopotamia as 56 Arabian miles or somewhat more, amounting to 336,000 Arabic feet which Norwood finds equal to 370,222 English feet. According to this the Arabic measurement of 827 A. D. was equivalent to 1° = 70.1 Eng. st. mi.

Norwood cites the Arabic astronomer, Alhazen, as taking the earth's circumference to be 240,000,000 paces which is per degree 333,333 Arabic feet or 367,283 English feet, or 1° = 69.58 Eng. st. mi.

The 500 stadia per degree given by Ptolemy in

---

[26] R. Norwood, *Sea-Mans Practice,* fifth edition, London, 1662, p. 34.

his *Geography* and by Posidonius as stated by Strabo, is interpreted by Snell and after him by Norwood as equivalent to 300,000 Alexandrian feet, which is 371,900 English feet, or 1° = 70.4 Eng. st. mi. This interpretation differs entirely from that of Hues.

Fernel's measurement yielded, according to Norwood, 68 Italian miles and 96 paces, or 68096 paces, where the pace is "more than five of our English feet." This would mean that 1° is more than 64.48 Eng. st. mi.

Norwood reports Snell in Holland as having found in a degree 342,000 Rhynland feet which is 353,306 English feet. According to this, Snell's measurement yields 1° = 66.91 Eng. st. mi.

It is remarkable that neither Edward Wright nor Richard Norwood refers to the earth's measurement carried out by Eratosthenes. In the above summary we are concerned, not so much with the validity of the interpretation of the various determinations in English measure, as we are with what Norwood thought the measurements were. We are endeavoring to ascertain English opinion on the subject, in the early part and middle of the seventeenth century.

Norwood's meridian measurement. This measurement, performed in 1635, was a notable achievement; the details of procedure are given in his

Sea-Mans Practice. In June, 1635, he made observations on the meridian altitude of the sun at the city of York, using a sextant of more than 5 feet radius. At the same time of the month, in 1633, he had taken similar observations in London, near the Tower. He found a difference of latitude of 2° 23'. He determined the distance between the two parallels to be 9149 chains. Reducing these data, he found in a degree of latitude 367,200 feet or 1° = 69.5 Eng. st. mi., an amount larger than Snell's, Wright's, Oughtred's and Fernel's, but smaller than the figures which he gave as due to Posidonius, Ptolemy, the ninth century Arabs, and Alhazen. Norwood's figure was only four tenths of a mile greater than the famous 69.1 miles found by Picard in 1671. Norwood counted in a degree of latitude 60 miles of 6120 feet each.

Norwood on navigation practice. Of interest to us is also Norwood's statement relating to the navigation practice in his day. In his "Dedicatory" to the *Sea-Mans Practice*, he states that notwithstanding the growth of the art navigation, "the way of finding distances at Sea, namely, by the Log and Line, is rather opinionative and conjectural then certain, being grounded upon this supposition, that the compasse of the World in any great Circle is 21600 Italian miles (as they call them) and that such an Italian mile contains 1000 Paces and every one of those fiue English feet:[27] And according to these measures they divide their Log-line." Here 60 such Italian miles make a degree; they are equivalent to 1° = 56.81 Eng. st. mi. We quote further:[28]

"There be three things (as I conceive) that have caused this errour to be so commonly received and tollerated. The one, for that it doth somewhat counterpoize another contrary errour in the Practice of Navigation, namely in the use of the Plain chart, for the errour which is there committed by making every parallel equal to the Equinoctial, and so every degree in them greater than they should be, is something moderated by this errour, whereby the measure of a degree is esteemed less than indeed it is . . . if two meridians be distant in the Equinoctial ten degrees, that is 600 miles, the same meridians in the Latitude of 35 degr. will be distant little more than 490 miles. Now if unto every mile we account according to the former experiment 6120 feet, then is the distance of those two meridians in that parallel neer 3,000,000 feet. In like sort in the Plain chart ten degrees of that parallel (as of all others) is made equal to ten degrees of the Equinoctial or Meridian: so that the distance of

[27] "Most unquestionably many, perhaps most, writers make use of a mile of 5000 feet, probably not being aware of the English foot having become longer than the Roman, and intending to use the Roman mile." A. DeMorgan, article "Mile" in the *English Encyclopaedia*.

[28] R. Norwood, *Sea-Mans Practice*, fifth edition, 1662, pp. 41, 42.

those two Meridians will upon the Plain Chart be 60 miles, but one of these miles contains onely 5000 feet, so that the distance is but 3,000,000 feet, equal to the former. And although these errours in other cases do not justly balance one another as in this example, yet that of the Plain Chart is alwayes something moderated by the other, . . . A second cause [seems] to be, for that men commonly desire to have their reckoning before their Ship (as they say) that they fall not with a place before they look for it;" . . . "a third cause of admiring and retaining this Errour seems to be, for that there hath been no way delivered from evident and certain grounds, for rectifying of it."

Did Norwood's value for the degree become known in England? Newton's alleged unfamiliarity in 1666 with the geodetic measure of Norwood is explained by Voltaire[29] on the theory that Norwood's value did not become known to English writers on navigation and scientific men because of the political upheavels of that time in England. James Wilson, in his essay on the history of navigation takes exception to Voltaire in the following important statement:[30]

[29] "Elemens de philosophie de Newton," *Oeuvres completes de Voltaire*, Vol. 28, Physique, Paris, 1819, p. 321.

[30] James Wilson, "Dissertation on the Rise and Progress of the Modern Art of Navigation," in Maseres' *Scriptores Logarithmici*, Vol. 4, 1801, p. 321, republished from John Robertson's *Elements of Navigation*, thirteenth edition, 1772.

"Norwood's measure . . . though it was not known to the great Sir Isaac Newton in his youth, was not buried in oblivion, on account of the confusions occasioned by our civil wars, as M. de Voltaire has been pleased to say; on the contrary, it has been constantly commended by our writers on Navigation: as, for example, by Mr. Henry Bond, soon after its publication, in a note at page 107 of the *Seaman's Kalendar*, . . . and by Mr. Henry Phillips, in his *Geometrical Seaman*, in 1652, and in his *Advancement of Navigation*, in 1657; and by Mr. John Collins, in his *Navigation by the Plane Scale*, in 1659; and by the Reverend Dr. John Newton, in his *Mathematical Elements*, in 1660; and by Mr. John Seller, in his *Practical Navigation*, 1669; and by Mr. John Brown, in his *Triangular Quadrant*, in 1671."

S. P. Rigaud[31] states that Sir Jonas Moore in his *Mathematical Compendium*, London, 1674, quotes Norwood's measure as a standard. We have seen it commended also in Samuel Sturmy's *Mariners Magazine*.[32]

Here are cited nine books referring to Norwood's earth's measurement, five of which appeared before

[31] S. P. Rigaud, *Historical Essay on* . . . *Sir Isaac Newton's Principia*, Oxford, 1838, p. 4.

[32] S. Sturmy, *Mariners Magazine*, third edition, 1684, p. 19, first edition, 1667.

1666. We have seen that Norwood's own books, the *Trigonometrie* and *Sea-Mans Practice* passed through several editions. Rigaud says the *Sea-Mans Practice* continued to be printed till 1732.

Edmund Gunter. He was the designer of Gunter's "chain" and was a widely known writer in his day. In his book, *Of the Sector, Crosse-staffe, and other Instruments*, 1624, the part devoted to "the measure of land by perch and acres," Gunter takes 320 perches (rods) equal to a mile; that is, in land surveying, he uses a mile of 5280 feet. But when writing on navigation he uses a mile of 5000 feet. In the part on the Sector, *written* before Snell's earth-measurement of 1617, Gunter takes one degree of latitude equal to 20 leagues or 60 miles (300,000 feet). In the part on the Cross-staff, written later, he refers to $1° = 60$ miles as the commen practice, but allows now "352,000 feet to a degree."[33] Fuller discussion follows later.

Outstanding results of this study. (1) A great variety of widely different estimates of the size of the earth is given in the books of Robert Hues, Edward Wright and Richard Norwood, due in part to uncertainties on the relative lengths of Greek, Roman, Arabic and modern units of length; (2) Snell's measurement of 1617 in Holland, aiming

---

[33] Of the *Works of Gunter*, the first edition appeared in 1624, the second in 1636, the third in 1653, the fourth in 1662, the fifth in 1673.

at great accuracy, was known to William Oughtred, Richard Norwood and W. Robinson; Norwood's measurement of 1636 was cited by many English writers on navigation; (3) The practical seamen and writers on navigation almost without exception took, in their practical calculations, a degree of latitude equal to 60 miles, the mile having 5000 feet, and the foot being either the modern English foot or an earlier somewhat shorter foot.

A hitherto overlooked inaccuracy in Pemberton. In 1728 Pemberton[34] referred "to the common estimate in use among geographers and our seamen, before Norwood had measured the earth, that 60 English miles were contained in one degree of latitude . . . . a very faulty supposition each degree containing about $69\frac{1}{2}$ of our miles." It is evident from the "$69\frac{1}{2}$" that the reference here is to the English statute miles of 5280 feet each. But our historical study shows that English seamen and geographers did not take the degree to be 60 English statute miles, but 60 older English miles of 5000 feet. The earliest writer we could find who stated that the degree was taken to be 60 *statute* miles was Oughtred in 1633. He was a clergyman, not a seaman, and in this statement did not represent the prevailing opinion and practice. A statement like

[34] Henry Pemberton, *A View of Sir Isaac Newton's Philosophy*, London, 1728, Preface.

TABULAR VIEW

The numerical values found in the six English publications already cited, and also seventeen other English publications most of which were issued before 1671, the year when the results of Picard's earth measurements were made public in France. The publications are arranged chronologically so as to exhibit the views held at different times.

AUTHOR AND DATES	WHAT WAS THE COMMON PRACTICE IN NAVIGATION AND GEOGRAPHY? THE AUTHOR'S ANSWER	ESTIMATES MADE BY THE AUTHOR OR BY AUTHORITIES CITED BY HIM	EQUIVALENCE IN ENG. ST. MI. PER 1°
Mandeville[1] fifteenth century		Writers on astronomy	79.6 (?)
Lindesay,[2] 1528	1 mile = 5000 feet	Astronomers, circumference = 31480 miles	82.8
Recorde,[3] 1551	1° = 60 miles, 1 mile = 5000 feet (?)		56.8 (?)
Cunningham[4] 1559	English mile = Italian mile		54.6 or 56.8
Digges,[5] 1591	Radius = 5011 Italian miles		82.8
Hues 1592, 1638, 1659	1° = 60 miles, 1 mile = 5000 English feet		56.8
		Aristotle, 1° = 1111.1 furlongs	126.2
		Strabo and Hipparchus, 1° = 700 furlongs	79.6
		Eratosthenes, 1° = $694\frac{4}{9}$ furlongs	78.9
		Posidonius and early Arabs, 1° = $666\frac{2}{3}$ furlongs	75.8
		Ptolemy and English, 1° = 500 furlongs	56.8
		The later Arabs, 1° = $566\frac{2}{3}$ furlongs	64.4
		Italians and Germans, 1° = 480 furlongs	54.6

[151]

TABULAR VIEW—*Continued*

AUTHOR AND DATES	WHAT WAS THE COMMON PRACTICE IN NAVIGATION AND GEOGRAPHY? THE AUTHOR'S ANSWER	ESTIMATES MADE BY THE AUTHOR OR BY AUTHORITIES CITED BY HIM	EQUIVALENCE IN ENG. ST. MI. PER 1°
Borough,[6] 1596		1° = 60 old miles, radius = $3436\frac{4}{11}$ miles	56.8
Cortes, 1596 Still sold in London in 1662	1° = 17½ or 16⅔ Spanish leagues; 1 Spanish league = 3 miles; 1 mile = 5000 feet		45.4 or 43.2
Davis[7] 1607	1° = 60 miles; 1 mile = 5000 feet		56.8
Wright 1610, 1657	1° = 17½ leagues; 1 league = 20,000 feet	Zamorano	66.3
		Wright himself, 1° = 18,312,621 feet	60.5
		Quotes estimates for radius ranging from 3000 to 8000 miles	49.6 to 132.2
Robinson[8] 1630?, 1633?		Snell	66.9
Oughtred 1633, 1660	1° = 60 miles; 1 mile = 5280 feet	Navigators	60
		The author (probably after Snell)	66¼
"Van Etten"[9] 1633, 1653, 1674		radius = 3436 ancient miles	56.8

Norwood 1631, 1636, 1662	1° = 60 miles; 1 mile = 5000 feet	Navigators	56.8
		Author's measurement, 1° = 60 miles. 1 mile = 6120 English feet. (This was commended by Bond, Phillips, Collins, J. Newton, Seller, Brown, Moore, Sturmy)	69.5
		Alhazen	69.6
		Ptolemy	70.4
		Fernel	64.5
		Snell	66.9
Gunter 1624, 1673	1° = 60 miles; 1 mile = 5000 feet		56.8
	1° = 60 miles = 20 leagues	Gunter's preference was Snell's value	66⅔
Foster[9a] 1661 Boyle[10] n.d. Leybourn[11] 1678 Members Roy.[12] Soc., 1672		German source	56.8
		1 mile = 5280 feet	93.3
		Members: 1° = 73 miles; 1 mile = 5000 feet. Picard	69.1

TABULAR VIEW—*Concluded*

AUTHOR AND DATES	WHAT WAS THE COMMON PRACTICE IN NAVIGATION AND GEOGRAPHY? THE AUTHOR'S ANSWER	ESTIMATES MADE BY THE AUTHOR OR BY AUTHORITIES CITED BY HIM	EQUIVALENCE IN ENG. ST. MI. PER 1°
Sturmy[13] 1667, 1678, 1684	1° = 60 miles; 1 mile = 5000 feet		56.8
Is. Newton[14] 1687, 1713, 1726		Richard Norwood Newton: 1 mile = 5000 feet; radius = 3923.16 miles (Picard)	69.5 69.1
Bernard[15] 1688	1° = 60 miles; 1 mile = 5280 feet		60
Stone[16] 1726	1 knot in log = 42 feet; i.e. 1 mile = 5000 feet		

[1] John Mandeville, in his *Travels*, English version, fifteenth century: "Aftre the auctoures of astronomye, 700 furlonges of erthe asweren to a degree of the firmament: and tho ben 87 miles and 4 furlonges." This yields 252,000 furlongs (stadia) for the earth's circumference. This is the larger of the two values, 250,000 and 252,000 stadia, obtained by Eratosthenes.

[2] Sir David Lyndesay in his poem *The Dreme*, 1528, lines 631-658.

[3] Robert Recorde, *Castle of Knowledge*, 1556. Copies from De Morgan in *Companion to the British Almanac*, 1836, p. 35.

[4] William Cunningham, *Cosmographicall Glasse*, London, 1559, p. 57.

[5] Thomas Digges, *Pantometria*, London, 1591, p. 43.

[6] William Borough, *Discourse of the Variation of the Compasse*, London, 1596, chapter 9.

[7] John Davis, *The Seamans Secrets*, London, 1607.

[8] W. Robinson's letter of June 12, [1603?] to William Oughtred, printed in S. P. Rigaud, *Correspondence of Scientific Men of the Seventeenth Century*, Vol. 1, Oxford, 1841, p. 12-15. Robinson writes: "If you have never read that book of Snellius, I would you would find leisure to peruse it; for if ever any man went the demonstration way (and labour there wants none in him) he hath done it."

9 "H. Van. Etten" (the French Jesuit Jean Leurechon), *Mathematical Recreations*, brought out in English translation at London in 1633, 1653, 1674. On page 219 of the 1653 edition, the radius of the earth "according to ancient traditions is 3436 miles" and the "circuit of the earth is 21600 miles."

9a *The Works of Edmund Gunter*, fourth edition, 1662, *The Sector Altered* by Samuel Foster, London, 1661, p.19.

10 Robert Boyle, *Works*, Vol. 2, p. 351.

11 William Leybourn, *Arithmetick*, fourth edition, London, 1678, p. 17. [First edition 1649].

12 Members of the Royal Society, in 1672, gave Picard's measurement in English miles as 73 miles of 5000 feet per degree. See Th. Birch, *History of the Royal Society*, Vol. 3, p. 3.

13 Samuel Sturmy, *Mariner's Magazine*, third edition, by John Colson, London, 1684, Bk. IV, p. 131, 61. The first edition appeared in 1667, the second in 1678.

14 Isaac Newton, *Principia*, Book III, Prop. 19; also Props. 10, 39.

15 Edward Bernard, *De mensuris et ponderibus antiquis libri tres*, Oxford, 1688, p. 202, describes (so says A. De Morgan in the *Penny Cyclopaedia*, Art. "Mile") the sea mile as coinciding with the statute mile. De Morgan states also that "the first actual measurement of roads in England, in statute miles, was made by John Ogilby, cosmographer to Charles II, and was published by him in 1675, under the title of *Britannia*."

16 E. Stone, *New Mathematical Dictionary*, London, 1726, Article "Log."

Oughtred's was made again in 1688 by Edward Bernard, a professor of astronomy at Oxford. It appears therefore that Pemberton's statement does not apply, as he claimed it did, to the ordinary seaman's practice on or before 1666, but it applies to a few scientific writers inclined to introduce improvements, of which, before 1666, Oughtred was the sole representative. Even among scientific men, as late as 1672, the use of the old mile was quite common. We have seen that Picard's measurement was translated into English miles at a meeting of the Royal Society as 73 miles of 5000 feet per degree. More than that, Newton himself in the *Principia*, Book III, Proposition 19, expresses Picard's value for the earth's radius in miles "reckoning 5000 feet to a mile." In two other places he uses "miles" without specifying which kind, but the context indicates that miles of 5000 feet are intended.[35] It is certain that in 1666 and long afterwards, practical seamen, generally, took one degree of latitude to be 60 miles of 5000 feet each. As late as 1726, E. Stone,[36] in his *New Mathematical Dictionary*, Article "Log,"

[35] *Principia*, Book III, Props. 10, 39.

[36] Stone's statement that the common practice among seamen continued to be the use of log-lines with knots 41⅔ or 42 feet apart, implying a mile of 5000 feet, is born out by the article "Log" in C. Hutton's *Mathematical Dictionary*, 1796, in *Rees's Cyclopaedia*, 1819, and the article "Navigation" in the *Edinburgh Encyclopaedia*, 1832.

states that "the common erroneous practice at sea" is to have the knots in the log-line only 42 feet apart (which stands for the theoretical 41⅔ feet obtained by dividing the 5000 feet in the mile by 120, the number of half-minutes in an hour), while as a matter of fact the distance between the knots "ought to be at least 50 feet," i.e., 6080 ÷ 120, 6080 being the number of feet in a modern nautical mile.

NEWTON'S GRAVITATIONAL CALCULATION OF 1665 OR 1666

Since the time of Kepler the hypothesis of a gravitational force acting inversely as the square of the distance between the attracting bodies was being entertained by some leading astronomers and mathematicians, but no one presented a proof other than the deduction of this law from Kepler's law that the square of the times of revolution of two planets vary as the cubes of their distances from the sun—a law, the accuracy of which was then in doubt. Newton when at his old home in the country, having gone there to escape the plague, was the first to subject the gravitational hypothesis to a scientific test. Unfortunately there is no contemporary record of the details of that test. In applying the hypothesis of gravitation acting inversely as the square of the distance to the earth

[157]

and moon, four observational constants were needed: (1) The exact time of one revolution of the moon relative to the stars; (2) The distance of the moon from the earth expressed in earth's radii; (3) The radius of the earth; (4) The distance a body falls from rest on the surface of the earth in one second. None of these values expressed in the usual units is an integral number, and therefore easily remembered. Newton nowhere states what constants he did use in 1665 or 1666. The values ascribed to him by later writers are mere guesses. The distance of the moon from the earth was estimated by the Greeks as a trifle less than 60 of the earth's radii. In his *Principia* (Book III Proposition 4) Newton takes 60. The distance a body falls from rest in a second is about 16.1 English feet. In the *Principia* Newton takes a more accurate value determined by Huygens from pendulum experiments, at Paris, and expressed in Paris feet.

Sources of information relating to the calculation of 1666:

I. We have a statement of Newton himself, in a written draft of the early history of his scientific discoveries, which was found by the astronomer Adams, about 1887, in the "Portsmouth Collection" of Newtonian papers. The manuscript is not dated, but is believed to have been written about

1714.[37] The original is cancelled and therefore, as W. W. R. Ball remarked, it is not indisputable evidence. However, it is true that the document is Newton's and in his hand-writing.[38]

II. A passage in the Preface of Henry Pemberton's *View of Sir Isaac Newton's Philosophy*, already alluded to.

III. A passage in the *Memoirs of the Life of Mr. William Whiston by himself*, London, 1749, Vol. 1, p. 35–38.

IV. The item in a note-book of Newton indicating an expenditure, "Gunter's Book and Sector to Dr. Fox, £0.5.0."[39]

Newton's Memorandum. We omit his reference to fluxions, the binomial theorem, optics, and quote simply the passage relating to gravity:

"And the same year [1665 or 1666] I began to think of gravity extending to ye orb of the Moon, and having found out how to estimate the force with w^{ch} [a] globe revolving within a sphere presses the surface of the sphere, from Kepler's Rule of the periodical times of the Planets being in a sesquialterate proportion of their distances from the centers of their Orbs I deduced that the forces

---

[37] W. W. R. Ball, *An Essay on Newton's Principia*, London, 1893, p. 7.

[38] *Portsmouth Collection*, Section I, Division XI, Number 41.

[39] D. Brewster, *Memoirs of Sir Isaac Newton*, Vol. 1, Chap. II, Edinburgh, 1860, pp. 27–29.

wch keep the Planets in their Orbs must [be] reciprocally as the squares of their distances from the
centers about wch they revolve: and thereby compared the force requisite to keep the Moon in her
Orb with the force of gravity at the surface of the
earth, and found them answer pretty nearly. All
this was in the two plague years of 1665 and 1666,
for in those days I was in the prime of my age for
invention, and minded Mathematicks and Philosophy more than at any time since. What Mr.
Hugens has published since about centrifugal forces
I suppose he had before me."

The important words in this passage are "*and
found them answer pretty nearly.*"

Pemberton's statement of 1728. We copy from
Pemberton's Preface three passages; part of the
last has been already quoted:

"It was in the very last years of Sir Isaac's life,
that I had the honour of his acquaintance . . . .
he engaged me to take care of the new edition he
was about making of his *Principia* [The third
edition, 1726]. This obliged me to be very frequently with him, and as he lived at some distance
from me, a great number of letters passed between
us on that account."

"Though his memory was much decayed, I found
he perfectly understood his own writings."

"Supposing therefore the power of gravity, when

[160]

extended to the moon, to decrease in the same manner, he computed whether that force would be sufficient to keep the moon in her orbit. In this computation, being absent from books,[40] he took the common estimate in use among geographers and seamen, before Norwood had measured the earth, that 60 English miles were contained in one degree of latitude on the surface of the earth. But as this is a very faulty supposition, each degree containing about 69½ of our miles, his computation did not answer expectation; whence he concluded, that some other cause must at least join with the action of the power of gravity on the moon. On this account he laid aside for that time any farther thoughts upon this matter."

Whiston's statement of 1749:

"I have heard him long ago, soon after my first acquaintance with him, which was 1694, thus relate, and of which Dr. Pemberton gives the like Account, and somewhat more fully, in the Preface to his Explication of his Philosophy: . . . . Taking this Postulatum, which had been thought of before, that such Power might decrease, in a duplicate Proportion of the Distances from the

[40] This statement, "being away from books," is not altogether in accordance with the fact, for we have seen that Newton recorded in a note-book the purchase of a few books during 1665–1666, including "Gunter's Book and Sector." See D. Brewster's *Memoirs*, Edinburgh, 1860, Vol. 1, Chap. II, pp. 27–29.

Earth's Center. Upon Sir Isaac's first Trial, when he took a Degree of a great Circle on the Earth's Surface, whence a Degree at the Distance of the Moon was to be determined also, to be 60 measured miles only, according to the gross Measures then in Use. He was, in some Degree, disappointed, ... Upon this Disappointment, which made Sir Isaac suspect that this Power was partly that of Gravity, and partly that of Cartesius's Vortices, he threw aside the Paper of his Calculation, and went to other Studies."

Purchase of "Gunter's Book and Sector." This item, entered in an expense list in a note-book of Newton, has never before been considered in connection with the law of gravitation. Some doubt exists as to which of Gunter's books is meant here. One of Gunter's publications was the *Canon logarithmorum*, a table of logarithms, 1620. In 1624 appeared in print Gunter's *Description of the Sector and Crosse-staffe and other Instruments*. As far as we have been able to ascertain, the description of the Sector and the description of the Cross-staff were never brought out as separate printed books. If Newton purchased the one, the other went with it. In 1624 appeared also the *Collected Works* of Gunter, in one moderate-sized volume, which was issued in later editions in 1636, 1653, 1662, 1673 and 1680. In the Sector, Gunter takes one degree of latitude equal to 20 leagues or 60 miles (i.e., 300,000 feet), the manuscript having been written several years before Snell made his measurements. But in the Cross-staff, which was written later, Gunter rejects 300,000 feet and accepts Snell's 352,000 feet, which is equivalent to $1° = 66\frac{2}{3}$ Eng. st. mi.

Discussion of these data. We have now presented the source-material bearing on Newton's calculation of 1666 to test the gravitational hypothesis. Whiston's statement appears to rest on that of Pemberton to whose Preface he specifically refers. In 1749 Whiston was eighty-two years old. Over half a century had passed since the time when he made the acquaintance of Newton, and twenty-two years after his death. It is quite possible therefore that Whiston was quite dependent upon Pemberton for the statement that Newton "took a Degree of a great Circle on the Earth's Surface . . . . to be 60 measured Miles only, according to the gross Measures then in Use." Be that as it may, neither Whiston nor Pemberton gives the important information as to the kind of mile that Newton used in his calculation, whether it was the mile of 5000 feet or that of 5280 feet. Pemberton's statement is self contradictory. He speaks of "$69\frac{1}{4}$ miles" as the correct measure of a degree, which in 1728 when he wrote, would mean a mile of 5280 feet. Hence the "60 miles" used in the

[163]

same connection must be 60 "statute miles." But this is in direct conflict with Pemberton's statement that Newton "took the common estimate in use among geographers and our seamen." We have shown that seamen almost always took for a degree 60 miles of 5000 feet each.

Let us now consider Newton's earth-moon calculation of 1665 or 1666. In view of Newton's purchase of "Gunter's book" it is very probable, almost certain, that he knew Gunter's estimate for the size of the earth, $1° = 66\frac{2}{3}$ Eng. st. mi., which is approximately Snell's value. If Newton used $66\frac{2}{3}$, he obtained 15.53 feet, instead of the correct experimental value of 16.1 feet as the fall of a body from rest in a second. This is an error of $3\frac{1}{2}\%$. Perhaps such a result would have elicited his remark that he "found them answer pretty nearly," especially as he must have known that, at best, the calculation was only approximate, on account of the uncertainties of his other experimental data, and of the fact that he had assumed the moon's orbit to be circular, when as a matter of fact it was approximately elliptical. We do not know that in 1666 Newton knew Norwood's value for the earth's meridian, but, if he used that value, the agreement of theory and experiment was even closer.

But suppose that, in some unaccountable way,

Newton overlooked both Norwood's and Gunter's values, what were the alternatives? If Newton had taken 60 miles of 5000 feet each, instead of the approximately correct figure of 69.1 miles of 5280 feet each, then instead of the experimental value of 16.1 feet of fall, he would have obtained from his calculations only 13.24 feet, an error of 18% or over one-sixth, which would be in sharp conflict with Newton's own statement that he "found them answer pretty nearly."

If it be argued in favor of Pemberton's statement, that one author on navigation, namely Oughtred, did refer to 60 English statute miles per degree as "taken" in navigation and that Newton might have seen the text, then, it must be noted also that in that very passage Oughtred points out the error of using only 60 statute miles per degree and he himself takes 66¼ such units. So, if Newton had seen this passage in Oughtred, he would have used 66¼ statute miles and obtained in his earth-moon calculation 15.44 feet in place of 16.1, which is an error only a bit over 4 per cent. He would have "found them answer pretty nearly."

It has been suggested that Newton may have chosen the value determined by Edward Wright, equivalent to 60.5 English statute miles to the degree. But if Newton consulted Wright's *Certain Errors in Navigation*, he would probably have noticed three things: (1) He would have found (as had Oughtred and Norwood) that Wright's determination was crude, as Wright himself admitted; (2) that Wright's historical survey disclosed extreme diversity of estimates of the size of the earth; (3) that in the most practical part of the publication (the translation of Zamorano) figures are given equivalent to $1° = 66.3$ Eng. st. mi. It is reasonable to suppose that if "60 miles" led Newton to "disappointment," he would try other values no less reliable which had come to his attention.

Suppose that, after all, Newton had used 60 statute miles per degree and, contrary to his own statement in the Portsmouth memorandum, had found as Pemberton claims that "his computation did not answer expectation," how long after Newton's return from the country to Cambridge is it reasonable to suppose that he could have remained ignorant of two facts firmly established in the English literature of his day, namely, the fact that writers such as Edward Wright and Richard Norwood had pointed out the great variety of different estimates of the size of the earth, and the further fact that Snell and Norwood had made careful measurements of the earth and had obtained results greatly exceeding 60 miles per degree, Norwood's results being quoted by many writers on navigation? How long could Newton have remained ignorant of these facts? In other lines of research Newton exhibited ability to select authors that were authorities—Oughtred in algebra, Wallis in arithmetic of infinities, Van Schooten in mathematical Miscellanies, Descartes and Barrow in geometry, Kepler in astronomy and optics. In no other field of science cultivated by Newton did he exhibit such lack of alertness in ascertaining the achievements of others and the common knowledge of the time, as is attributed to him by his biographers in the matter of the size of the earth. Are the biographers right? It is difficult to see how in 1666 or 1667 Newton could escape finding fairly accurate values for the radius of the earth. On the contrary it is easy to see that he found his computation, as he says, to "answer pretty nearly." Later statements of Newton indicate that he was halted, perhaps as early as 1666, by a theoretical difficulty relating to the mutual gravitational attraction of spherical bodies which, when understood, might reveal perhaps that his law was only approximate. This difficulty he was not able to clear up in 1666 and for many years following. Another theoretical difficulty which troubled Newton later, as we shall see, was the shape of the earth and the variation of the distance a body falls in a second, in different latitudes. It

[167]

may be due to the first of these difficulties that Newton in 1666 laid the matter aside.

NEWTON'S APPARENT INDIFFERENCE DURING 1666–1685 TO EARTH MEASUREMENTS

Newton's edition of the Geography of Varenius.[41] This book was brought out in Latin, at Cambridge in 1672. For it "I have described schemes" Newton wrote Collins.[42] The first edition had appeared in Holland in 1650, and was considered the best book on geography of that time. Another Cambridge edition, with Newton as editor, came out in 1681. A third edition in English translation was issued after the death of Newton, in 1736, in which the translator remarked: "The reason why this great man took so much care in correcting and publishing our author, was because he thought him necessary to be read by the audience while he was delivering lectures upon the same subject from the Lucasian chair."

Varenius in his Geography devotes a whole chapter (Chapter IV) of eleven pages to the size

[41] *Bernhardi Vareni Geographia generalis, in qua affectiones generales Telluris explicantur, summâ curâ quam plurimis in locis emendata, et XXXIII Schematibus novis, aere incisis, unâ cum Tabb. aliquot quae desiderabantur aucta et illustrata. Ab Isaaco Newton Math. Prof. Lucasiano apud Cantabrigienses. Cantabrigiae 1672.*

[42] S. P. Rigaud, *Correspondence of Scientific Men of the Seventeenth Century,* Oxford, Vol. 2, 1841, pp. 322, 335.

of the earth. He makes one of the earliest careful reviews of the different methods of determining the circumference of our globe. He cites attempts to estimate its dimensions from the time of Anaximander and Aristotle to his own day. He explains eleven ways of measuring, the last three of which dispense with any astronomical observations, being purely "terrestrial." The various values obtained are not reduced to English units. The 252,000 stadia which Eratosthenes obtained for the circumference, Varenius estimates at 315,000 Roman miles of 1000 paces each. As we have seen, the pace contained 5 feet, so that the 315,000 Roman miles were close to 315,000 English miles of 5000 feet each, which is equivalent to $1° = 81$ Eng. st. mi. The value for the circumference which Cleomedes ascribes to Posidinius is given as 240,000 stadia. Reducing this as we did the value of Eratosthenes, we obtain $1° = 77.8$ Eng. st. mi. Varenius cites the Arabic determinations at 56 or $56\frac{1}{2}$ Arabic miles to a degree of latitude. The stadia which Ptolemy used are interpreted by Varenius as different from the stadia of Eratosthenes. Taking 32 stadia per German mile, Ptolemy's 180,000 stadia for the earth's cricumference yields 5625 German miles of 22,800 Rhyland feet each which we interpret as equivalent to $1° = 69.3$ Eng. st. mi. Snell's measurement of the year 1617 is given as 28,500 perches or 342,000 Rhyland feet per degree, which yields us 1° = 66.3 Eng. st. mi. Varenius critically examined Snell's work and introduced a correction which reduced the 28,500 perches to 28,473 perches. Snell's measurement indicated a thoroughness which challenged attention.

None of the values given in Newton's edition of Varenius is as low as 60 English statute miles per degree.

Jean Picard's measurement. In 1671 Jean Picard[43] published the results of a triangulation which he had carried on in France with improved instruments. Here for the first time were angles measured with a telescope and cross wires. The determination at once commanded attention in England as well as in France. It amounted to 1° = 69.1 Eng. st. mi.; it was larger than Snell's and almost identical with Norwood's. On January 9 and February 1, 1672, Picard's value was mentioned at meetings of the Royal Society of London. Newton was not present at the first meeting and perhaps not at the second.[44] However, an account of Picard's measurements appeared in the *Philosophical Transactions* for 1675, Volume 10, page 261, and the

[43] J. Picard, *La measure de la terre*, Paris, 1671.

[44] S. P. Rigaud, *Historical Essay on . . . Sir Isaac Newton's Principia*, Oxford, 1838, p. 9.

following year in Volume 11, page 591. These data seem to give the time when Picard's work became generally known to scientific men in England. On January 22, 1677–1678, the astronomer royal Flamsteed[45] at Greenwich wrote to Bernard, "When I came hither first we had frequent discourse about measuring the degree from this place, but having got an account of his, we find it needless, he has been so careful." It is not generally known that from August, 1668, to August 4, 1686, plans for measuring the earth with improved instruments were discussed at many meetings of the Royal Society, his Majesty, King Charles II, having expressed a desire that such a measurement be carried out.[46] Hooke, and toward the last Halley, were urged to undertake the work. According to Hooke[47] the plans were not executed because the necessary funds were not available. That Picard's measurement received attention in England appears also from the twelfth edition of Norwood's *The Seamans Practice*, 1673, page 59, where there was inserted, after Norwood's death the paragraph: "About the year 1672 Monsieur Picart has published an account in French concern-

[45] S. P. Rigaud, *Historical Essay on . . . Sir Isaac Newton's Principia*, Oxford, 1838, p. 10.

[46] Th. Birch, *History of the Royal Society*, Vol. 2, pp. 313, 398, 400, 403, 413, 440, 446, 478, 483; Vol. 3, p. 3; Vol. 4, pp, 150, 151, 491, 497.

[47] Th. Birch, *History of the Royal Society*, Vol. 4, p. 150.

ing the measure of the earth, a breviate whereof may be seen in the *Philosophical Transactions*, Number 12. wherein he concludes one degree to contain 356,184 English feet, nearly agreeing to Norwood's experiment." Newton appears to have been regularly supplied with the Philosophical Transactions by Oldenburg,[48] and as Rigaud adds, "it does not appear possible, that a matter of so much real importance could have escaped his attention for a long series of years."

The variation of gravity due to the earth's rotation about its axis was investigated by Newton, theoretically, about 1671. Newton says in a letter to Halley,[49] July 14, 1686: "Some time above fifteen years ago. . . . . I calculated the force of ascent at the equator, arising from the earth's diurnal motion, in order to know what would be the diminution of gravity thereby. But yet to do this business right, is a thing of far greater difficulty than I was aware of." This "diminution of gravity" indicates that the radius of the earth is not the only one of four "constants" entering the earth-moon test of the law of gravitation which calls for the exercise of caution; the force of gravity at the earth's surface is one of these "constants."

[48] S. P. Rigaud, *Historical Essay on* . . . *Sir Isaac Newton's Principia*, p. 10.
[49] S. P. Rigaud, *Historical Essay* . . . *on Sir Isaac Newton's Principia*, Appendix, p. 40.

It is different for different latitudes. If Newton at this time did not also speculate on the figure of the earth, he did so in a letter which he wrote in 1680 to Thomas Burnet of Cambridge who had just published in Latin his *Theory of the Earth*, a famous book in its day. Burnet held that the earth is egg-shaped, elongated at the poles. Newton writes:[50] "I am most inclined to believe it spherical, or not much oval. . . . . If its diurnal motion would make it oval, that of Jupiter would much more make Jupiter oval. . . . . What may be argued from ye dimensions of ye earth's shadow collected by lunar eclipses I cannot tell, nor what from ye measure of ye earth answering to a degree in several latitudes, not knowing how exactly those measures were made or the latitudes of places taken." Here is a reference to different earth's measurements familiar to him from Valerius' *Geography* and probably also other sources.

When did Newton repeat his calculation of the earth's attraction of the moon? It is not definitely known. The recomputation was made at some period, for, it is given in the *Principia*, Book III, Proposition 4, Parisian feet being used there as the unit of length. If in 1666 he compared his computed value with the experimental "and found them answer pretty

[50] Brewster, *Memoirs of Sir Isaac Newton*, Vol. 2, 1860, pp. 357, 358.

nearly," as he himself says, then the repetition with Picard's figure for the earth's radius was of no great significance. If for Newton's version of the 1666 test, we substitute that of Pemberton, according to which the computation of 1666 "did not answer expectation," then a recomputation would be more significant. In the absence of definite information on this recomputation, certain biographers and historians of science indulged in the delights of "romancing in science" in the manner shown in our Introduction. That Newton actually did repeat the computation about the time when Picard's value was announced follows from Newton's letter to Halley, June 20, 1686, in which he explains that he was not indebted to Robert Hooke for the suggestion of the law of inverse squares in gravitational attraction, that in "papers writ (I cannot say in what year, but I am sure some time before I had any correspondence with Mr. Oldenburg, and that's) above fifteen years ago, the proportion of the forces of the planets from the sun, reciprocally duplicate to their distances from him is expressed, and the proportion of our gravity to the moon's conatus recedendi a centro terrae is calculated, though not accurately enough."[51] "About fifteen years ago" would be about 1671.

[51] W. W. R. Ball, *An Essay on Newton's Principia*, London, 1893, p. 157.

His correspondence with Oldenburg began in 1672.[52] Newton did not mean his early work of 1666, for about three weeks later[53] (letter of July 14, 1686) he again refers to his paper "which I told you was writ some time above fifteen years ago, and to the best of my memory was writ eighteen or nineteen years ago," and in this same letter he mentions another date, "twenty years ago" (i.e., 1666) as the time when he "gathered" the "duplicate proportion" from Kepler's theorem. Evidently his "fifteen years ago" or more, and his "twenty years ago" were two different periods. That the paper of "above fifteen years ago" was not written in the year of the plague (1666) is evident also from its contents. Newton says it also dealt with the "moon's phase," the "limit of the sun's parallax," the diminution of gravity due to the earth's rotation—all Newtonian studies nowhere assigned to this period.

From Newton's own statement we are safe in concluding that the second calculation was made sometime between 1667 and 1672.

Why was there, after about 1672 a further delay of about thirteen years in announcing the law of gravita-

[52] David Brewster, *Memoirs of Sir Isaac Newton*, Vol. I, Edinburgh, 1860, pp. 44, 46; S. P. Rigaud, *Historical Essay on . . . Sir Isaac Newton's Principia*, 1838, p. 52.

[53] W. W. R. Ball, *An Essay on Newton's Principia*, London, 1893, p. 165.

tion? The available facts indicate two reasons for the delay. One was that Newton was engaged in other studies and had abandoned "philosophy" (*i.e.*, natural philosophy) because of the controversies to which his optical experiments had led him after 1672. "I had for some years last been endeavoring to bend myself from philosophy to other studies in so much that I have long grutched the time spent in that study unless it be perhaps at idle hours sometimes for a diversion," writes Newton to Hooke in a letter dated November 28, 1679.[54] Newton refers to this matter again in a letter to Halley, June 20, 1688: "Philosophy is such an impertinently litigious Lady, that a man had as good be engaged to lawsuits, as to have to do with her. I found it so formerly, and now I am no sooner come near her again, but she gives me warning."[55] And yet, as Brewster says,[56] at the very time when Newton was engaged in controversy with Dutch professors, he was occupied, "for a diversion" perhaps, with the subject of the moon's libration.

The second reason for Newton's delay is one of vital interest and historical importance. From his own statements we gather that he was held

[54] W. W. R. Ball, *An Essay on Newton's Principia*, London, 1893, p. 141.
[55] W. W. R. Ball, *An Essay on Newton's Principia*, London, 1893, p. 158.
[56] D. Brewster, *Memoirs*, Vol. 2, 1860, Chapter VI, p. 112.

back by theoretical difficulties in the earth-moon test.

"Though not accurately enough." Newton does not explain this phrase which we have quoted above from his letter of June 20, 1686. It was written at a time when Newton dealt severely with his own hypotheses. Thus he found the variation of gravity due to the earth's rotation "a thing of far greater difficulty than I was aware of." His early thoughts on the libration of the moon were discarded in 1673 for "he apprehended a better cause."[57]

If, about 1671, Newton used Norwood's 367,200 feet per degree determined in 1635, and assumed the moon's distance from the earth to be 60 earth's diameters, and the time of one revolution of the moon 27d. 7h. 43 min., the calculated fall of a body from rest in a second would be 16.19 English feet. Picard's 57060 toises or 365,100 feet per degree would yield a fall of 16.096 feet. These values are close to the experimental values. Are they close enough?

The 16.096 feet and 16.19 feet are obtained on the assumption, which Newton probably made about 1671 and which he does make in his *Principia* (Book III, Proposition 4), that the earth is stand-

[57] Newton's letter to Oldenburg, 1673, Brewster, *Memoirs*, Vol. 1, p. 112.

ing still, is a sphere and that the orbit of the moon is circular. But he knew that these assumptions were only approximately true and proceeded in the *Principia* to make allowance for them.[58] We have seen that about 1671 Newton concluded on theoretical grounds that the experimental values for the distance a body falls from rest in unit time on the earth's surface must vary with the latitude. But in 1671 no experiments, indicating the amount of variation were available, not even Richer's pendulum experiments at Cayenne. Moreover, Newton later found the theory of that subject "far more difficult than he was aware of." Still more disconcerting was the further fact (to be discussed more fully presently) that he did not know in 1671 exactly how a sphere attracts an outside particle. All these theoretical considerations which, as we know, demanded his attention when he wrote his *Principia*, may have caused him to say that the test made about 1671 came out "not accurately enough."

[58] Newton discusses sources of error in the earth-moon test in the *Principia* Book III, Prop, 3, 4, 19, 25, and in the corollaries of Prop. 37, and also in the early part of the *System of the World*. It is well known that Newton spent much effort in years after the first publication of the *Principia* in deducing a completer theory of the moon's motion on the hypothesis of the law of gravitation.

AN ESSENTIAL STEP IN PROVING THE LAW OF GRAVITATION

As J. C. Adams and J. W. L. Glaisher have shown, the problem of the attraction of a sphere engaged Newton's attention. He saw, as others of his day did not see, that a fairly close agreement between calculation and experiment in the earth-moon test would not overcome the difficulties of the gravitation hypothesis. A more serious difficulty than that of the motion of the earth presented itself to him. In applying the law of inverse squares of the distances, how should the distances be measured? Hooke and others had guessed that it should be measured from center to center. By "center" was probably meant "center of mass." Apparently, this measurement from center to center was guessed to be true whatever the shapes of the attracting bodies might be and whatever the variation of mass-density in a body might be. Newton saw the danger involved in these assumptions and the need of profounder study. As yet it was not evident that the law of inverse squares was anything more than an *approximation* to the real processes of nature. The absence of thorough examination of the "center to center" hypothesis even for spheres composed of concentric layers each of uniform density, prevented Newton from applying the law of gravitation unreservedly to the motion of heavenly bodies and of projectiles near the earth.

Not until 1685 did Newton settle this mathematical question to his satisfaction. We proceed to quote from Newton's letters and from his works in support of this explanation of his long delay. We omit the account, how Newton was led to resume temporarily gravitational problems by his and Dr. Done's visit[59] to Christopher Wren in 1677, and by Hooke's invitation to Newton in a letter of November 24, 1679, to communicate to the Royal Society his thoughts on his own (Hooke's) view of celestial motions,[60] how, in August 1884 Halley[61] went to Cambridge to ask Newton what would be the curve described by the planets on the supposition that gravity diminished as the square of the distance, how Newton was led thereby to write out for Wren the solution (an ellipse) which he had found in 1677, and how Newton then (1684) fortunately continued his investigations which were a rough draft of the beginning of the first book of the *Principia*.[62]

On April 28, 1686, the manuscript for the larger

[59] W. W. R. Ball, *An Essay on Newton's Principia*, London, 1893, p. 155.
[60] W. W. R. Ball, *An Essay on Newton's Principia*, London, 1893, p. 140.
[61] W. W. R. Ball, *An Essay on Newton's Principia*, London, 1893, p. 27.
[62] W. W. R. Ball, *An Essay on Newton's Principia*, London, 1893, p. 28.

part of the *Principia* was presented by Dr. Vincent to the Royal Society, ready for print. This act constituted an announcement of the law of gravitation. Hooke immediately claimed this law as his discovery and that he had given Newton the first hint of it. A controversy arose between Newton and Hooke. Newton stated his claim of independent work in letters to Halley. It is these letters that furnish data on the history of his great discovery.

Newton refers to his investigation of 1685 on the attraction of a sphere in letter to Halley of June 20, 1686:[63]

"That I never extended the duplicate proportion lower than to the superficies of the earth, and before a certain demonstration I found last year, have I suspected it did not reach accurately enough down so low; and therefore in the doctrine of projectiles never used it nor considered the motions of the heavens; and consequently Mr. Hooke could not from my letters, which were about projectiles and the regions descending hence to the centre, conclude me ignorant of the theory of the heavens. That what he told me of the duplicate proportion was erroneous, namely, that it reached down hence to the centre of the earth."

[63] W. W. R. Ball, *An Essay on Newton's Principia*, London, 1893, p. 157.

The part on our present question is the passage "before a certain demonstration I found last year, have I suspected it [the law of inverse squares] did not reach accurately enough down so low." That is to say, before 1685 Newton suspected that the law of inverse squares was a mere approximation to the truth. Newton's "projectiles" is a reference to his prediction made in a letter to Hooke, dated November 28, 1679, that a body falling from a height would pass "to the east side of the perpendicular,"[64] and in which Newton made no mention of the law of inverse squares.

Newton refers to his "demonstration" again in the same letter in the following passage:[65]

"For as Kepler knew the orb to be not circular but oval, and guessed it to be elliptical, so Mr. Hooke, without knowing what I have found out since his letters to me, can know no more, but that the proportion was duplicate quam proximè at great distances from the centre, and only guessed it to be so accurately, and guessed amiss in extending that proportion down to the very centre, whereas Kepler guessed right at the ellipsis. And so Mr. Hooke found less of the proportion than Kepler of the ellipsis. There is so strong an objection against the accurateness of this proportion,

[64] W. W. R. Ball, *An Essay on Newton's Principia*, London, 1893, p. 143.
[65] W. W. R. Ball, *An Essay on Newton's Principia*, London, 1893, p. 158.

that without my demonstrations, to which Mr. Hooke is yet a stranger, it cannot be believed by a judicious philospher to be any where accurate."

It is to be noted that Newton's "demonstration" yielded results which he had not expected and which came to him as a surprise. His words imply that he regarded this "demonstration" as an essential part in establishing the law of inverse squares as an exact law. A third time Newton touches this point in a long postscript to the above letter:[66]

"But if you consider the nature of the hypothesis, you will find that gravity decreases upwards, and can be no other from the superficies of the planet than reciprocally duplicate of the distance from the centre, but downwards that proportion does not hold. This was but an hypothesis, and so to be looked upon only as one of my guesses, which I did not rely on; but it sufficiently explains to you, why in considering the descent of a body down to the centre, I used not the duplicate proportion."

The matter is alluded to again in a passage of one of the copies of Newton's tract, *De Motu*, which was the name given to the first drafts of the early part of the *Principia*[67] which implies that

[66] W. W. R. Ball, *An Essay on Newton's Principia*, London, 1893, p. 161.
[67] W. W. R. Ball, *An Essay on Newton's Principia*, London, 1893, pp. 35, 56.

Newton knew that at a great distance from the earth's center, gravity might be taken to vary inversely as the square of the distance from the center, but that he was not then certain whether the same law held for points near the earth's surface.

An interesting statement is found in Newton's *Principia* (Book III, Proposition 8): "After I had found that the force of gravity towards a whole planet did arise from, and was compounded of the forces of gravity towards all its parts, and towards every one part, was in the reciprocal proportion of the squares of the distances from the part: I was yet in doubt, whether that reciprocal duplicate proportion did accurately hold, or but nearly so, in the total force compounded of so many partial ones. For it might be that the proportion which accurately enough took place in greater distances, should be wide of the truth near the surface of the planet, where the distances of the particles are unequal, and their situation dissimilar. But by the help of proposition 75. and 76. book I. and their corollaries, I was at last satisfy'd of the truth of the proposition, as it now lies before us."

CONCLUSION

It is an interesting fact that while Newton in his letters, when speaking of gravitation, repeatedly refers to the theorem of the attraction of a sphere, he nowhere even mentions the radius of the earth. To him the size of the earth does not seem to have been the cause of serious uncertainty. The quotations from Newton's letters of 1686 have the advantage over statements of Pemberton and Whiston, of being in Newton's own words, written not long after the events had transpired and at a time when Newton was mentally at his best. Pemberton knew Newton when Newton's "memory was much decayed," and Whiston wrote his own *Life* many years after the death of Newton when Whiston was an octogenarian. When Pemberton states that Newton's computation of 1666 did "not answer expectation" and that Newton laid the subject aside until Picard's data reached him, Pemberton probably is giving simply an echo of Newton's "though not accurately enough," distorted in the course of oral transmission and by the passage of years. It will be remembered that this statement was applied to Newton's second calculation of about 1671, when he was embarrassed, not by wrong earth measurements, but by theoretical difficulties which he did not overcome until many years later.

Newton's own written statements, taken by themselves, constitute a consistent though in some places incomplete account of the progress of his great discovery. Pemberton's statement, when applied to the calculation of 1665 or 1666, contradicts Newton. It contradicts also the historical facts which we have presented. Pemberton claims that navigators used 60 English statute miles to the degree of latitude, but as a matter of fact they used 60 miles of 5000 feet each. Pemberton says that Newton's computation of 1666 "did not answer expectation," which is not in accordance with Newton's own written statement. Pemberton says that in 1665 and 1666 Newton was "absent from books," but Newton himself recorded the purchase of a few works, including "Gunter's book."

It follows that the explanation of Newton's delay of about twenty years in announcing the law of gravitation was due to theoretical difficulties involved in the earth-moon test. We have shown that the delay could not have been due to any gross error in the value for the size of the earth used in the calculation in 1666.

In conclusion we cannot forego quoting from an article in the London *Times* of March 19, 1927, written by the astronomer H. H. Turner, and containing historical matter which, on questions of theory, is supported by the statements of Newton himself:

"In fact Newton was stimulated by Halley's visit of 1684 to return to the whole question of gravity which had been intermittently in his thoughts since he saw the apple fall in the autumn of 1666. At that time the general idea of an attraction varying as the inverse square of the distance occurred to him, but he saw grave difficulties in its complete application of which lesser minds were unconscious. The most important of these he did not overcome until 1685, 19 years after the falling of the apple. It was that of linking up the attraction of the earth on a body so far away as the moon with its attraction on the apple close to its surface. In the former case the various particles composing the earth (to which individually Newton hoped to extend his law, thus making it universal) are at distances from the moon not greatly different either in magnitude or direction; but their distances from an apple differ conspicuously in both size and direction. How are the separate attractions in the latter case to be added together or combined into a single resultant? and in what "centre of gravity," if any, may they be concentrated? The beautiful theorem which he discovered, showing that the total attraction of a sphere of an apple at its surface, just as on a distant satellite, is accurately concentrated at the centre of the sphere, came as a complete surprise to him and must have given him great joy. It put the law of gravity on an entirely new footing, converting what had been possibly only a crude approximation for planetary bodies into an accurate and universal law. The discovery of it was a great achievement, representing an important step in integral calculus, and it is probable that the final success in solving it was only the sequel to many failures."

NEWTON'S FLUXIONS

NEWTON'S FLUXIONS

FLORIAN CAJORI, Ph.D.

Professor of the History of Mathematics in the University of California

TRAVELLERS to Mürren in the Berner Ober-
land behold the sight of massive mountains
with three prominent peaks, the Eiger, the
Mönch and the Jungfrau. In contemplating the
massive scientific achievements of Newton, three
peaks stand out conspicuously, the researches on
gravitation, on optics, and on fluxions.

In all three, the first stages of creative work
belong to the period immediately preceding or
following the time when Newton took his degree
of Bachelor of Arts at Trinity Collge, Cambridge.
During parts of the years 1665 and 1666 the college
was closed on account of the plague; Newton left
Cambridge for his boyhood home at Woolthorpe
where he led a life of contemplation. He was less
subject to distraction than he would have been in
our day with its cinema and radio. On May 20,
1665,[1] he committed to writing his first thoughts on
fluxions. It was then that he introduced the
notation of dots placed over letters ("pricked
letters") to indicate "fluxions," the letters with-

---

[1] D. Brewster, *Memoirs of Sir Isaac Newton*, Edinburgh, 1860, Vol. 1, p. 22.

out the dots representing "fluents." A fluxion
was not an infinitely small quantity, as was in-
correctly stated by many early writers of Newton's
time, but a finite value, a velocity. In modern
phrasing, a fluxion $\dot{x}$ is a time-derivative, $\dfrac{dx}{dt}$, x being
the fluent. In 1666 Newton prepared two further
memoranda in his note-book, relating to fluxions.
These memoranda were never published, but were
kept in the Macclefield Collection of Newtonian
manuscripts. Later Newton prepared a tract, *De
analysi per aequationes*, which he communicated in
1669 to Isaac Barrow who sent it to John Collins
who, in turn, circulated it among friends of Newton. This was not printed until 1711. In 1671
Newton composed the *Methodus fluxionum*, originally intended as an introduction to an edition
of Kinckhuysen's Algebra, but it was first printed
in English translation in 1736. The basic principles of fluxions were set forth in Newton's
Principia, 1687. As the notation was not given,
readers did not recognize in fluxions, an important
tool for solving problems on velocities, tangents,
curvatures, areas and volumes.

What really constitutes the earliest printed account of Newton's fluxions, including his notation,
appeared in Wallis' *Algebra* of 1693, pages 390–
396. This account was written by Newton himself. It explained fluxions sufficiently for mathe-

maticians to acquire and use the process. In 1695 De Moivre published in the *Philosophical Transactions*, No. 216, an article in which he used $\dot{x}, \dot{y}, x, \ddot{y}$. It is well known that at first the method employed by Newton involved fixed infinitesimals. But in the Introduction to the *Quadratura curvarum*, published in 1704, Newton aimed to develop his theory without the use of infinitely small quantities. Both in his *Principia* and *Quadratura curvarum*. he used "prime and ultimate ratios," which involve the concept of limits, though in a form differing from that adopted by mathematicians later. These prime and ultimate ratios do not contemplate primarily one constant which one variable approaches. The prime and ultimate ratios are ratios of two quantities just springing into being or else vanishing. Only secondarily does Newton, in applying his theory to finding the fluxion of x^n, for example, consider in the right member of his equations what we would call the limit of a ratio. Newton was really considering the ratio of two quantities, each of which was approaching the limit zero, rather than the limit of one quantity that was the ratio of two quantities. In England it required the talent of Benjamin Robins to transform Newton's fluxions of 1704 into a calculus founded on limits; on the continent the transformation exercised the ability of D'Alembert who laid the emphasis upon the limit of a ratio, and gave only secondary consideration to the ratio of limits that were zero.

The history of fluxions and their interpretation in terms of modern mathematics have been thoroughly worked out, except on one point. The question has been debated by writers on the European continent, whether Newton performed partial differentiation and dealt with partial differential equations. The settlement of this question is not as easy as it might seem, for in early days the technical language of fluxions and the calculus and symbols to express the different shades of meaning, were not so fully developed as they are now. It is therefore easy to misinterpret an author or to read into his writings more, or perhaps less, than what the author meant to express. In 1856 Hermann Weissenborn of Bonn issued his *Principien der höheren Analysis*, giving a critical historical account of the development of analysis from Leibniz to Lagrange. In one place he discusses Newton's treatment of differential equations, as found in his *Method of Fluxions*. In Problem II case III Newton solves a fluxional equation involving three fluxions. Newton says:[2]

"The Resolution of the Problem will soon be

[2] Sir Isaac Newton, *The Method of Fluxions*, translated into English by John Colson, London, 1736, p. 41.

dispatch'd, when the Equation involves three or more fluxions of Quantities. For between any two of those Quantities any Relation may be assumed, when it is not determined by the State of the Question, and the Relation of their Fluxions may be found from thence; so that either of them, together with its fluxion, may be exterminated. . . . .

Let the Equation proposed be $2\dot{x} - \dot{z} + \dot{y}x = 0$; that I may obtain the Relation of the Quantities x, y, and z, whose Fluxions $\dot{x}, \dot{y}$ and $\dot{z}$ are contained in the Equation; I form a Relation at pleasure between any two of them, as x and y, supposing that $x = y$ or $2y = a + z$, or $x = yy$, etc. But suppose at present $x = yy$, and thence $\dot{x} = 2\dot{y}y$. Therefore writing, $2\dot{y}y$ for $\dot{x}$, and yy for x, the Equation proposed will be transform'd into this: $4\dot{y}y - \dot{z} + \dot{y}y^2 = 0$. And thence the Relation between y and z will arise, $2yy + \frac{1}{3}y^3 = z$. In which if x be written for yy, and $x^{\frac{3}{2}}$ for y^3, we shall have $2x + \frac{1}{3}x^{\frac{3}{2}} = z$. So that among the infinite ways in which x, y, and z may be related to each other, one of them is here found, which is represented by these Equations, $x = yy$, $2y^2 + \frac{1}{3}y^3 = z$, and $2x + \frac{1}{3}x^{\frac{3}{2}} = z$."

Weissenborn (p. 39) interprets the equation solved here as a partial differential equation and declares Newton's solution to be incorrect, as may be seen by trial, he says. That this is the solution

of a partial differential equation was held also by
the Swiss historian Heinrich Suter,[3] and the German historian Moritz Cantor[4] in the third volume
of his *Vorlesungen*, but in the Preface Cantor re-
tracts the statement, only to adopt it again in the
second edition that appeared three years later.[5]
In sharp opposition to Weissenborn's interpretation are a tract by E. Tischer[6] of Leipzig, notes by
G. Eneström[7] of Stockholm, and a recent article
by Edmund Hoppe[8] of Göttingen.

It seems to us that the criticisms against Weissenborn made by Tischer, Eneström and Hoppe are
entirely valid as regards Newton's differential
equation of more than two variables in the *Method
of Fluxions*. It is not a partial differential equation, but a total differential equation. Moreover,
Newton's result cited in our quotation is a correct
solution.

Tischer and Hoppe go much further and claim

[3] H. Suter, *Geschichte der Mathematischen Wissenschaften*, Vol. 2, 1875, p. 74.

[4] M. Cantor, *Vorlesungen über Geschichte der Mathematik*, Vol. III, 1898, p. 166.

[5] M. Cantor, *Vorlesungen über Geschichte der Mathematik*, Vol. III, 2 ed., 1901,
p. 172.

[6] Ernst Tischer, "Ueber die Begründung der Infinitesimalrechnung durch
Newton und Leibniz," *Jahresbericht des Nicolaigymnasium in Leipzig*, Leipzig,
1896, pp. 37–39.

[7] G. Eneström, *Bibliotheca Mathematica*, Vol. 4, 1905, p. 400; Vol. 11, 1912,
pp. 172–173.

[8] E. Hoppe, "Die Entdeckung der partiellen Differentialgleichungen,"
Archiv für Geschichte der Mathematik, der Naturwissenschaften und der Technik,
Vol. 30, 1927, pp. 158–165.

that Newton's fluxions, being time-derivatives, do not admit of partial differential expressions. We quote Hoppe's statement (p. 159):

"When Newton has an equation in several fluents (we would say in variable magnitudes), that is, in x, y, z, u, etc., he derives the fluxions by assuming that these variables are all *functions of one and the same variable magnitude*, for example, of the time. Then he marks the fluxion of x by $\cdot$, of y by $\dot{y}$, etc., so that $\dot{x}$ means in our notation $\dfrac{dx}{dt}$, $\dot{y} = \dfrac{dy}{dt}$, $\dot{z} = \dfrac{dz}{dt}$. Accordingly, if Newton had chosen to write his fluent equation briefly $f(x, y, z, \ldots) = u$, he would have meant by this, that $x, y, z, \ldots$, u are functions of t, but not . . . that u is a function of the independent variables $x, y, z, \ldots$ The $x, y, z, \ldots u$ were themselves functions of the variable t, the time or of the temperature or some similar variable, and f signified only that an equation existed between these functions. If Newton wished to represent $\dfrac{dy}{dx}$, he had to write $\dfrac{dy}{dx} = \dfrac{dy}{dt} \div \dfrac{dx}{dt} = \dot{y} \div \dot{x} = a \div 1$, where a is a magnitude measured according to the unit of the fluxions. . . . In this theory of fluxions no path was open to partial differential equations."

[197]

Tischer expresses this idea very tersely: "The concern here is not with a function of several independent variables, but with several functions of one and the same independent variable."

It seems to us that Tischer and Hoppe did not derive their views from Newton's own statements. They started from preconceived notions and read these into the Newtonian theory. They interpreted Newton as teaching that when t changes all the other variables necessarily change with it. On that assumption there could be no partial derivative, no partial differentiation or integration and no partial differential equation. But this is too narrow a view of the Newtonian theory. If $u = f(x, y)$, then there is nothing in Newton's exposition to prevent y being considered constant when x varies. He had no symbol for partial differentiation, but he might have written $\dot{u}_x$ and meant by it the velocity of u when x varies and y is constant. Just as $\dot{u}$ means $\dfrac{du}{dt}$, so $\dot{u}_x$ would mean the time-derivatives of u when x varies and y is constant; accordingly $\dot{u}_x / \dot{x}$ would mean $\dfrac{\partial u}{\partial x}$.

That Tischer's and Hoppe's interpretations of Newton's fluxions are in conflict with Newton's actual procedure appears from the following quotation from the *Method of Fluxions*, which explains

[198]

the differentiation of an implicit function in x and y:[9]

"If the Relation of the flowing Quantities x and y be $x^3 - ax^2 + axy - y^3 = 0$; first dispose the Terms according to x, and then according to y, and multiply them in the following manner.

Mult.	$x^3 - ax^2 + axy - y^3$	$-y^3 + axy - \begin{array}{c} a\,x^2 \\ + x^3 \end{array}$
by	$\dfrac{3\dot{x}}{x} \cdot \dfrac{2\dot{x}}{x} \cdot \dfrac{\dot{x}}{x} \cdot 0$	$\dfrac{3\dot{y}}{y} \cdot \dfrac{\dot{y}}{y} \cdot 0$
makes $3\dot{x}x^2 - 2a\dot{x}x + a\dot{x}y$ *		$-3\dot{y}y^2 + a\dot{y}x$ *

The sum of the Products is $3\,\dot{x}x^2 - 2a\dot{x}x + a\dot{x}y - 3\dot{y}y^2 + a\dot{y}x = 0$, which Equation gives the Relation between the Fluxions $\dot{x}$ and $\dot{y}$. For if you take x at pleasure, the Equation $x^3 - ax^2 + axy - y^3 = 0$ will give y. Which being determined, it will be $\dot{x}:\dot{y}::3y^2 - ax:3x^2 - 2ax + ay$."

Here Newton clearly allows x to vary while y is constant, and *vice versa*, a procedure which Tischer and Hoppe would hold to be a violation of Newtonian theory. As a matter of fact, Newton does not exclude partial differentiation. Except in language and symbols, and in the use of fluxions instead of differentials, we have in the above example the exact modern procedure of finding the total differential of an implicit function $f(x, y)$, yielding

[9] Sir Isaac Newton, *Method of Fluxions*, edited by John Colson, 1736, p. 21.

[199]

the important relation $\dfrac{\partial f}{\partial x} \, dx + \dfrac{\partial f}{\partial y} \, dy$. We have

$$\frac{\partial f}{\partial x} = 3x^2 - 2ax + ay, \frac{\partial f}{\partial y} = -3y^2 + ax.$$

Newton performed also partial integrations. He considered the problem: A fluxional equation being given, to find a fluent equation. "As this Problem is the Converse of the foregoing, it must be solved by proceeding in a contrary manner."[10] He gives the solutions of several examples, each involving partial integrations.

Thus the fundamental processes of partial differentiation and partial integration occur regularly in Newton's exposition, written by him as early as 1671.

[10] *Method of Fluxions*, p. 25.

SIR ISAAC NEWTON

By C. E. Dallin (in bronze)

This is the only statue of Newton known in the United States. It is in the Library of Congress overlooking the Main Reading Room.

NEWTON'S WORKS IN ALCHEMY
AND CHEMISTRY

NEWTON'S WORK IN ALCHEMY AND CHEMISTRY

LYMAN C. NEWELL, Ph.D.

Professor of Chemistry in Boston University

CLASSIFICATIONS are sometimes misleading. Newton is frequently called an alchemist, but he was not an alchemist in the usual meaning of the term with its unethical implications. He is also called a chemist, though he certainly was not a chemist in the modern sense of the word. If it were necessary to classify him at all, we would have to call him a natural philosopher, or more exactly, an experimental natural philosopher. Throughout his long scientific career he was an investigator of natural phenomena —physical, astronomical and chemical. And whenever possible, he stated his conclusion in a mathematical generalization.

Newton is usually classified as a mathematician. But his field was not enclosed by a mathematical fence. Mentally he was an inquirer, an experimenter, a philosopher—a lover of all knowledge. He was interested philosophically in all kinds of natural phenomena—resistance of the air, ebb and flow of the tides, movements of the heavenly

[203]

bodies, motion of all kinds, colors of all varieties and in all places, and especially changes in minerals, ores, and metals. Moreover he always sought order, system, law. As an experimental philosopher, too, he abhorred speculation. Indeed, whenever he indulged in speculation, he usually put it in the form of a query not a declaration. So in interpreting Newton's work in any field, especially the less productive ones, we must think of him as a philosopher, searching experimentally for a fundamental interpretation of broad relations in natural phenomena.

Like other learned men of his times, Newton was deeply interested in all branches of contemporary knowledge. It is my purpose in this paper to give an account of the experimental work in chemistry actually done by Newton and to present a survey of his activities as a natural philosopher in the extensive, though rather sterile, field of the chemistry of his times.

Newton was sent to Grantham (in 1655) when he was a mere lad. Here he attended the King's School until he left to enter Cambridge in 1661. In Grantham he lived with a Mr. and Mrs. Clark. The house was demolished long ago but the School is still conducted in a restored structure. Mr. Clark was an apothecary and doubtless Newton became familiar with the shop and its chemical contents. Several authorities, thinking probably of the initial interest of Davy, Scheele, and Liebig years later, ascribe Newton's interest in chemistry to this youthful association with the apothecary. Such a conclusion is gratuitous. There is no documentary evidence that Newton was more than a casual observer of the apothecary, his manipulations, and his chemicals. As a matter of fact, we have ample evidence that during this period Newton, like most boys of his age, was fully occupied in "making things." Among these mechanical contrivances was a water-clock which was in running order long after Newton left Grantham; a windmill which was fixed to the roof of the Clark's house so the wind could easily fill the sails; and a paper lantern which he used when he went to school in the winter. Newton as a school boy was not limited in his interests or activities. Indeed we have abundant evidence that even in these early days Newton definitely showed certain qualities which characterized his scientific career. The construction of boyish contrivances was concrete evidence of his experimental skill, the constant gazing at things in the heavens and on the earth was a natural employment of his powers of observation, the sudden fits of protracted labor were expressions of his reserve mental power, the apparent idleness was really his reflection, inner

[205]

questioning, mental preoccupation. No, Newton did not begin his scientific career in an apothecary shop!

By the time Newton had completed his studies in the King's School in Grantham and was ready to enter Trinity College, Cambridge, he was potentially an experimental natural philosopher—not a mathematician, not a physicist, not a chemist, but an unconscious lover of all scientific knowledge in its fundamental relations and modes of expression. He entered Trinity College in 1661, was elected a Scholar in 1664, received his B.A. in 1665, was made a Fellow in 1667, and received his M.A. in 1668. Owing to the plague, Trinity College was closed in 1667 and Newton was away about two years. In 1669 he was made Lucasian Professor of Mathematics.

Newton remained at Trinity College till 1696, when he became Warden (and in 1699 Master) of the Royal Mint. Newton's activities in chemistry were confined to the thirty-five years he was connected with Trinity College as student, fellow, and professor. His work in mathematics, astronomy, and optics is well known because the original accounts have long been available in historical documents and published books. Unfortunately the nature and extent of Newton's work in chemistry is not well known. Some biographers describe it briefly in more or less general sentences. Others dispose of it casually or ironically. Some complacently pass it along from earlier accounts which were not based on facts, indeed not even verified by accessible documents.

What are the sources of information about the chemistry and alchemy of Newton? The three main ones are (1) two of Newton's notebooks, one in the J. Pierpont Morgan Collection and the other in the Portsmouth Collection, (2) letters and documents containing accounts of his work, records of purchases, etc., and (3) books from his library, some of which are annotated. Scattered items and reports supplement or verify the main sources.

Examination of these sources leads unreservedly to certain conclusions:—

(1) Newton had a laboratory in or near his room in Trinity College where he performed many experiments in alchemy and chemistry from about 1661 to 1696.

(2) He consulted books on alchemy in the University library and copied items from them not only for help in performing experiments but for future use either in reading or experimenting.

(3) Many of his experiments involved metals.

(4) He bought many books of older alchemists and contemporary writers, read them conscientiously, annotated them, and copied many portions.

(5) He corresponded and consulted with his contemporaries, especially Boyle and Locke. He likewise argued with some of his contemporaries, conspicuously Hooke (Boyle's collaborator).

(6) He worked hard to discover some generalization which would explain or correlate baffling chemical phenomena, such as transmutation, combustion, and respiration.

(7) In his ardent desire to find a generalization, he proposed innumerable queries about the cause of chemical phenomena, the relation of diverse phenomena, the nature of acids, and the purification of substances, particularly metals.

Let us consider in detail some of the material on which these conclusions are based.

One of Newton's notebooks, which has been in the J. Pierpont Morgan Collection for several years, gives some information about the nature of Newton's earliest interest in chemistry. Through the courtesy of the J. Pierpont Morgan Library and the editorial skill of Dr. David Eugene Smith an account[1] of this notebook is available. Confining attention to the strictly chemical portions we find in the first part of this book a list of recipes, apparently from some country physician, and directions for performing simple chemical tricks. Dr. Smith concludes that this part of the book seems to

[1] Greenstreet's *Isaac Newton*, 1927, p. 16.

belong to the period of about 1655–1658 (age thirteen to sixteen). Judging from the character of the items we willingly agree with Dr. Smith in assigning them to a period of preadolescence. Here are the "strictly chemical" items.

"*How to make Allum water*

Take a quart of water and boyle it in a quarter of a pound of Allum, seeth it untill it be molten, and let it stand a day. wth this water wet over ye pictures y^t you intend to colour for it will keepe ye colours for sinking into ye paper, and make them shew fairer, and continue ye longer wth out fading You must let ye paper dry of itselfe before you lay yor colours on it or wet it againe for some paper needs four or 5 wetings."

"*How to make gum water*

Take cleane water and put gum Arabic a little into it, let it stand till ye gum be dissolved, and let it not bee too thick for you cannot work well wth it, nor too thin for it will not bind fast enough. wth this water temper your colours befor you lay them on."

"*To make lime water*

Take unslackt lime and cover it with water an inch thick let it stand a night and power of ye cleare water in ye morning, and keepe it in a cleane thing for yor use. wth this water you must temper yor sap greens when you would have a blew coulour of it."

"To make water of sope ashes

Steepe sope ashes a night in raine water, in ye norning power of ye clearest. this is to temp^r yor brasill wth."

"To melt mettle quickly yea in a shel

Make a bed or laying of metle, and on it make a other bed wth powder of brimstone salt peeter and sawdust. and like quantitie of either then put a fire to ye said powder wth a burning charcole and it will bee in a mass."

There are recipes for making many colors including one which anticipates a current mode, viz.

"A Colour for faces

Lay on ye cheekes little spotts of lake or red lead y^n come all over it with white, and a little lake, shaddow it wth lamblack or umber, and white lead."

Others equally unimportant make up the balance of the chemical portion. Of the "certaine tricks" one example will suffice.

"To turne waters into wine (Into Claret)

Take as much hockwood as you can hold in yo͏ʳ
mouth w͏ᵗʰ out discovery, tye it up in a cloth, and
put it in yo͏ʳ mouth, then sup up some wather and
champe ye hockwood 3 or 4 times and doe it out
into a glass."

Clearly this portion of the notebook belongs to
the unoriginal period of the copyist and is evidence
only of Newton's interest in unusual phenomena
more or less chemical.

The second portion, which was written about
1659 is "a word list consisting of a classification of
topics under a partial scheme of knowledge."
Among the sub-heads two are conspicuous— "(7)
Of the elements. Chap. 7." and "(16) Of Min-
eralls. Chap. 16." Dr. Smith says "there is no
statement as to whether or not they [the whole
list] referred to some book which Newton had been
reading or were designed to represent some scheme
of knowledge that he had worked out in another
manuscript," so we are left in doubt about the
source and purpose of these items. However,
certain conclusions may be drawn. In general,
it has long been customary for young men of a
certain type to prepare an elaborate scheme of self-
education. For example, two famous chemists,
Joseph Black and Humphrey Davy, did exactly the

[211]

same thing. Perhaps Newton had the same idea in mind. In any case, he pursued an elaborate, more or less systematic, plan in his subsequent studies. In particular, elements and minerals interested Newton throughout his long life. His books have many references to the traditional seven elements, he tried repeatedly to transmute metallic elements, and his interest in mineral appears repeatedly in his letters and notes from his youth to his last days in the Royal Mint. So regarding the chemical features of this early notebook, we conclude in spite of the trivial items that it represents certain early chemical interests and displays some fundamental traits of Newton.

Newton lived while at Trinity College in rooms near the great gate. His laboratory was nearby. A relative named Humphrey Newton, who acted as his assistant and amanuensis from 1683 to 1689 has left a graphic description of Newton's habits of work. He says in part:

"About 6 weeks at spring, and 6 at ye fall, ye fire in the elaboratory scarcely went out, which was well furnished with chymical materials as bodyes, receivers, heads, crucibles, etc., which was made very little use of, ye crucibles excepted, in which he fused his metals; he would sometimes, tho' very seldom, look into an old mouldy book wch lay in his elaboratory. I think it was titled

Agricola de Metallis, the transmuting of metals being his chief design, for which purpose antimony was a great ingredient. Near his elaboratory was his garden. . . . . " From another source we learn that "this garden was the space between the road and the college on the right-hand side on entering the great gate at Trinity College, and contained his chemical laboratory."

Unfortunately only a little is known about Newton's first years in Cambridge. There is no doubt however that much of his time was spent in experimental work. This letter of Newton's assistant shows that Newton must have had a laboratory containing furnaces in working order long before 1683. In support of this conclusion we have some evidence. Notebooks and records of Newton's show that he spent much time during his early days at Cambridge polishing lenses and doing experiments in chemistry and optics. A striking bit of direct evidence on this point is a letter written by Newton soon after he was obliged to leave Cambridge in 1665 (temporarily on account of the plague) in which he expressed regret at being deprived of his books and the use of his laboratory apparatus, and at being interrupted in his experiments. It seems highly probable, therefore, that Newton built and equipped a laboratory at Trinity College soon after he entered and began experiments in chemistry.

During his enforced absence from Cambridge for about two years Newton was not idle. Indeed this period was exceptionally fruitful. He had time to experiment and reflect and his work culminated in fundamental discoveries in physics, viz. color and gravitation. Records show that he also performed many chemical experiments, despite the enforced removal from his laboratory in Cambridge, and bills prove "that during this period he bought magnets, compasses, glass bubbles, drills, and so on, and also prisms and putty." There are also bills for chemicals bought during August and September, 1668. And during the time (1668–1670) he was constructing his first telescope, we know by a record that in April, 1669, "he spent quite considerable sums of money on chemicals, furnaces, and a 'theatrum chemicum.'" Perhaps this "theatrum chemicum" was the actual copy of Ashmole's *Theatrum Chemicum Britannicum* published in 1652 and now in the superb collection of Dr. Edgar F. Smith of Philadelphia. Possibly it was, as Brewster implies, the 6-volume book published in 1659–61 by Lazarus Zetznerus and purchased by Newton in 1669 for £18s 6d.

Having established the fact that Newton started chemical experimenting in his laboratory soon after he entered Trinity College in 1661, let us abandon the attempt to follow his chemical work chronologically, and consider instead certain salient features of his contributions to chemistry.

Newton's book entitled *Opticks* which was published in 1704 is almost exclusively devoted to physical phenomena and their interpretation. It contains, systematically arranged, the substance of the papers on light which had appeared in the *Philosophical Transactions*. Besides these papers it includes many "Queries," i.e., speculations mainly in the form of questions. Some of these queries relate to chemical phenomena. Sir J. J. Thompson says about them, "When, as in one of the queries, he discusses chemical questions, he revels in details known only to those who have spent long hours in a chemical laboratory." These queries are a mine of suggestions. One in particular—No. 31—contains the substance of what has come to be regarded as a separate contribution to Newton's work in chemistry. It is entitled *De Natura Acidorum*. Other queries relate to fire and flame—the age-old question of the nature of combustion.

Newton's paper entitled *De Natura Acidorum* is only about two pages long. It is one of the few chemical papers Newton formally published. Evidently it pleased editors and readers, because it is included in all the early editions of Newton's works. This paper must have been written subsequently to 1687 because it contains references to the *Principia*. The paper is not a descriptive account of acids, but a succession of speculations on the nature of affinity, particularly the varying affinity of salt radicals, as we call them today. This paper is incorporated by Newton in Query 31 (as just stated) in the third book of the *Opticks*. He says in part:

"Qu. 31. Have not the small particles of bodies certain powers, virtues, or forces, by which they act at a distance, not only upon the rays of light for reflecting, refracting, and inflecting them but also upon one another for producing a great part of the phenomena of nature? For it is well known that bodies act one upon another by the attractions of gravity, magnetism, and electricity; and these instances show the tenor and course of nature, and make it not improbable but that there may be more attractive powers than these. For Nature is very consonant and conformable to herself. How these attractions may be performed I do not here consider. What I call attraction may be performed by impulse, or by some other means unknown to me. I use that word here to signify only in general any force by which bodies tend towards one another whatsoever be the cause. For we must learn from the phenomena of nature what bodies attract one another, and what are the laws and properties of the attraction, before we inquire the cause by which the attraction is performed. The attractions of gravity, magnetism, and electricity reach to very sensible distances, so [as] have been observed by vulgar eyes, and there may be others which reach to so small distances as to escape observation; and perhaps electrical attraction may reach to such small distances even without being excited by friction.

"For when salt of tartar runs *per deliquium*, is not this done by an attraction between the particles of the salt of tartar, and the particles of the water which float in the air in the form of vapours? And why do not common salt, or salt petre, or vitriol, run *per deliquium*, but for want of such an attraction? Or why does not salt of tartar draw more water out of the air than in the certain proportion to its quantity, but for want of an attractive force after it is satiated with water? And whence is it but from this attractive power that water which alone distills with a gentle lukewarm heating will not distil from salt of tartar without a great heat? And is it not from the like attractive power between the particles of oil of vitriol and the particles of water, that oil of vitriol draws to it a good quantity of water out of the air, and after it is satiated draws no more, and in distillation lets go the water very differently? And when water and oil of vitriol poured successively into the same vessel grow very hot in the mixing, does not this heat argue a great motion in the parts of the liquors? And does not this motion argue that the parts of the two liquors in mixing coalesce with violence, and by consequence rush towards one another with an accelerated motion? And when aquafortis or spirit of vitriol poured upon filings of iron, dissolves the filings with a great heat and ebullition, is not this heat and ebullition effected by a violent motion of the parts and does not that motion argue that the acid parts of the liquor rush towards the parts of the metal with violence, and run forcibly into its pores till they get between its outmost particles, loosen them from the main mass and set them at liberty to float off into the water? And when the acid particles which alone would distil with an easy heat will not separate from the particles of the metal without a very violent heat, doth not this confirm the attraction between them?"

Newton in this paper, to repeat, is really speculating on affinity. In modern terms his paper may be summarized about as follows:

In his long query on elective attractions, he considers the small particles of bodies as acting upon one another at distances so minute as to escape observation. When salt of tartar deliquesces, he supposes that this arises from an attraction between the saline particles and the aqueous particles held in solution in the atmosphere, and to the same attraction he ascribes it that the water will not distil from the salt of tartar without great heat. For the same reason sulphuric acid attracts water powerfully, and parts with it with great difficulty. When this attractive force becomes very powerful, as in the union between sulphuric acid and water, so as to make the particles "coalesce with violence" and rush towards one another with an accelerated motion, heat is produced by the mixture of the two liquids. In like manner, he explains the production of flame from the mixture of cold fluids, the action of fulminating powders, the combination of iron filings with sulphur, and all the other chemical phenomena of precipitation, combination, solution, and crystallization, and the mechanical phenomena of cohesion and capillary attraction. He ascribes hot springs, volcanoes, fire-damps, mineral coruscations, earthquakes, hot suffocating exhalations, hurricanes, lightning, thunder, fiery meteors, subterranean explosions, land-slips, ebullitions of the sea, and water-spouts, to sulphureous steams abounding in the bowels of the earth, and fermenting with minerals or escaping into the atmosphere, where they ferment with acid vapours fitted to promote fermentation. In commenting on *De Natura Acidorum* a keen critic says:

[219]

"Newton is here but considering the operation of the force of residual affinity, which is not only unexplained to the present day but rarely considered. Speculation on these subjects today is not less vague than it was in Newton's time. Modifying his language but slightly, to reduce it to modern terms, we can but realize that little advance has been made in our understanding of the phenomena—although we have an exact and abounding knowledge of fact which is astounding compared with that of Newton's day. We need a Newton with the perspicacity to order our knowledge into a philosophy."

The chemical queries relating to fire, flame, vapour, and heat were revised in 1716 and 1717: hence we may regard them as containing the most mature opinions of Newton. He considers fire as a body heated so hot as to emit light copiously, red hot iron being nothing else than fire, and a burning coal likewise only redhot wood. In one of his notebooks, he says "flame is nothing but exhalation set on fire, and [that] a burning coal and a burning flame differ only in rarity and density." "Flame," he adds, "is nothing but a company of burning little coals dispersed about in the air." We must not overlook the significance of these words of Newton. Up to his time, and indeed until the time of Lavoisier (1742–1794), fire was believed by most chemists to be two-fold, viz. a combustible principle and a ponderable material. Newton was the first to shake these views. To him fire was not a ponderable substance. His recorded words mean clearly "that every strongly heated and glowing substance burns; that red-hot iron or wood may be called fire; and that those substances which emit much smoke burn with a flame." Unfortunately Newton's views, like those of Rey, Hooke, Mayow, and Lemery, were overlooked and the development of chemistry was consequently delayed nearly a century.

Newton like his predecessors, and especially his contemporaries Hooke, Mayow, Boyle, and Hales, thought too much and experimented too little in this baffling field of combustion. Newton had been thinking about it long before the *Opticks* was published because he wrote a letter to Boyle in 1679 "in fulfillment of a long deferred promise." The views he presents to his friend, he characterizes as "indigested and unsatisfactory" to himself and he adds, that "as it is only an explication of qualities that is desired" he "sets down his apprehensions in the form of suppositions."

It is perfectly clear why Newton put his views about fire in a query. Like all investigators from Rey to Lavoisier, Newton could not proceed far toward the complete experimental interpretation of combustion until one fundamental discovery was made and promulgated, viz. the relation of oxygen to air. No one could doubt that if oxygen had been discovered in Newton's time, Newton himself with his tremendous power of generalization would have anticipated Lavoisier in his great discovery of the rôle of oxygen in chemistry.

One more point about these queries deserves comment. They are speculations but they are not crude guesses or wild predictions. Newton put these views in the form of queries "because" he says, in the *Opticks*, "I am not yet satisfied about it for want of Experiments." Note the capital *E*. Do we not have here a glowing example of Newton the experimental natural philosopher?

In 1701 Newton published a paper in the *Philosophical Transactions* of the Royal Society (*Scala graduum caloris. Calorum Descriptiones & sigma* (No. 270 (1701), pp. 824–9). It is not a chemical paper, strictly speaking, but it is very closely related to chemistry. In it Newton describes a thermometer made with linseed oil, which had as fixed points the temperature of melting snow and that of the human body. It contained a comparative scale of temperature from melting ice to a small coal fire. The following are the principal points of the scale:

DEGREES OF HEAT	EQUAL PARTS OF HEAT	
0	0	Heat of the winter air when water begins to freeze.
1	12	The greatest heat at the surface of the human body and that at which eggs are hatched.
2	24	Heat of melting wax.
3	48	The lowest heat at which equal parts of tin and bismuth melt.
4	96	The lowest heat at which lead melts.
5	192	The heat of a small coal fire not urged by bellows. The heat of a wood fire is from 200 to 210.

This instrument is an interesting example of the accuracy of Newton's observations. He adopted the melting point of ice but not the boiling point of water as a basis, because he found that the boiling point varied, and he was unable to connect this variation with barometric pressure, despite the excellent work of his contemporary Boyle in this field. In this paper Newton incorporates two important generalizations. The first (modified in 1818 by Dulong and Petit) was that the rate of cooling at any moment of a warm body is proportional to the difference between the temperature of the body and of the surrounding medium. The second was that when a body is melting or evaporating, its temperature remains constant.

The corpuscular idea so fully presented in the *Opticks* seems almost inseparable from Newton. We find it cropping out in many places, often

[223]

unrelated to one another and having no relation whatever to light. One example must suffice, viz., Newton's statement about atoms:

"It seems probable to me that God in the beginning formed matter in solid, massy, hard, impenetrable, moveable particles, of such sizes and figures, and with such other properties and in such proportion, as most conduced to the end for which He formed them; and that these primitive particles, being solids, are incomparably harder than any porous bodies compounded of them; even so very hard as never to wear or break in pieces, no ordinary power being able to divide what God Himself made one in the first creation. While the particles continue entire they may compose bodies of one and the same nature and texture in all ages; but should they wear away, or break in pieces, the nature of things depending on them would be changed. Water and earth composed of old worn particles and fragments would not be of the same nature and texture with water and earth composed of entire particles in the beginning. . . . God is able to create particles of matter of several sizes and figures, and in several proportions to the space they occupy, and perhaps of different densities and forces. . . . At least, I see nothing of contradiction in all this. . . . . Now, by the help of these principles, all material things seem to have been composed of the hard and solid particles above mentioned—variously associated, in the first creation, by the counsel of an intelligent agent."

This statement about atoms seems almost forbidding until we examine it closely. Setting aside the assignment of a first cause, Newton is not far from certain aspects of our modern views of the constitution of matter. Indeed, if this statement about atoms, as well as many of the Queries in the *Opticks*, was stripped of the teleological trappings and re-written in modern terms, we would be compelled to appraise Newton's views as close approximations to our present interpretations of the constitution and behavior of matter.

It should not be overlooked that Newton was performing chemical experiments while he was accumulating material for his *Opticks*. Documentary evidence has already been cited about his chemical and alchemical work up to 1687. Correspondence with Locke and Boyle shows he was deeply interested in alchemical transmutations in 1692 and thereabouts. There is also a record of chemical experiments made (about 1692) on the properties and action of barm and on the distillation of salts of metals. Other records give accounts of experiments "resumed in April, 1695, and continued to February, 1696."

In 1696 Newton was appointed Warden of the

Royal Mint. He retained his connection with the Mint until his death in 1727—a period of thirty-one years, equal to the time spent in Trinity College.

Newton took his new duties seriously. Hard work was necessary because the debased silver coinage was causing much suffering and stirring up popular dissatisfaction. "The ability, the industry and the strict uprightness of the great philosopher," says Macaulay, "speedily produced a complete revolution throughout the department which was under his direction." And a contemporary who had business with Newton and could appreciate his merits at first hand said "well had it been for the publick, had he acted a few years sooner in that situation."

For three years Newton labored in the nation's cause, and in 1699 the recoinage was complete. Instead of producing fifteen thousand pounds' worth of silver per week, Newton and his co-workers had been able to increase the yield to one hundred and twenty thousand pounds' worth per week. The superior work of Newton was recognized, and in 1699 he was appointed Master of the Mint, a high office which paid between twelve hundred and fifteen hundred pounds per annum and was regarded as a commanding position in the nation, especially in its economic, scientific, and social aspects.

Doubtless Newton's friend, Montague, who had been loyal to him throughout vexatious disputes with astronomers and mathematicians, was moved to recommend Newton to the King for appointment partly because of Newton's integrity and industry. An added reason was Montague's conviction that Newton's knowledge of metals and his skill in metallurgy would be technically useful to the Mint.

Doubtless Newton was the best man available for the chemical and metallurgical work to be done at the Royal Mint. It is a fact, definitely recorded, that Newton had been working on metals for about thirty years. And items in the Portsmouth Collection of Newton's manuscripts, notebooks, and books (soon to be considered) show that Newton did many experiments with metals and indicate that he must have acquired exceptional skill and knowledge as a metallurgist. No doubt this skill was continuously used in the early days at the Royal Mint. Perhaps too, his unsatisfied desires in alchemy found a convenient opportunity for application in the congenial surroundings of the Royal Mint, though of this we have no record.

In preparing this paper, I expected to find an abundance of information about Newton's chemical and metallurgical work at the Royal Mint. Much to my astonishment preliminary search showed that information was scanty and scattered. To be sure there was a paper on the temperature of melting metals, but nothing whatever about processes of smelting, assaying, refining, and the numerous chemical operations normally performed in a mint. We know he worked incessantly because his letters tell of "absorption in his King's business," and voluminous reports on coinage in his own handwriting point to assiduous labors. We know further that he "devised methods for water-marking paper and melting down silver bullion." But where, I asked myself many times, is the account of the work of Newton the chemist while he was Master of the Royal Mint? The answer finally came from the Royal Mint itself. Through the courtesy of Dr. S. Brodetsky of Leeds University I was given a letter of introduction to Colonel Robert A. Johnson, Deputy Master and Comptroller of the Royal Mint. In response to my inquiry Colonel Johnson replied as follows:

"Royal Mint, London, E. 1.
13th October, 1927.

My dear Sir,

. . . . As regards Newton, I am afraid our information is exceedingly scanty. For instance, you enquire whether Newton actually made use of his chemistry in metallurgical and assaying processes here at the Mint. The answer is, alas, that a careful search was made in the library of the Royal Society at the time of the Grantham celebrations in the spring of this year with a view to tracing some record of such application to Mint work, but without success.

Next, in our archives here there is practically no original material connected with Newton's mastership of the Mint. It seems that when the Mint was moved from the Tower to the present site early in the nineteenth century, such documents as may have been preserved up to that time were handed over to the Record Office and, except for one solitary paper, we have nothing here in Newton's own hand. Even this exception—though it is accompanied by a statement 'original document in the hand writing of Sir Isaac Newton'—has not, so far as I am aware, ever been authenticated and anyhow is of minor interest, since it is merely a statement of gold and silver struck in the Tower from 1599 to 1675. There are, it is true, a few papers at the Record Office, but they really do not help at all. We have also a number of references in our "Record Books" here which are signed by Newton, but these records are simply a series of copy books which was continued during some centuries, and are our only unprinted source of historical information, none of them being really relevant to what you are searching for. Not only so, but a late Superintendent of ours, Sir Edward Rigg, was an indefatigable student of minting and was also the author of the article on Newton in the *Dictionary of Political Economy*.[2] If you refer to this volume, you will find that Rigg specifically remarks in his article on the silence of the Mint Records with regard to Newton's doings here."

Hence we must abandon regretfully this unproductive source of information about Newton's contribution to chemistry during a long period in which we would naturally look for the culmination of many preceding years of study and experimenting.

There is ample documentary evidence that Newton was deeply interested in alchemy throughout the thirty-odd years he was at Trinity College in Cambridge. Moreover the evidence shows that he performed many experiments in his own laboratory in his efforts to transmute metals into one another. The most interesting though not the most convincing piece of evidence is a letter Newton wrote to his young friend Francis Aston on May 18, 1669—only four years after Newton graduated from Trinity College. This letter is so important I quote the parts bearing on metals and alchemy.

"9. Observe the products of nature in several

2 First edition, 1899, Vol. III, p. 18.

places, especially in mines, with the circumstances of mining and of extracting metals or minerals out of their oare, and of refining them: and if you meet with any transmutations out of their own species into another, (as out of iron into copper, out of any metall into quicksilver, out of one salt into another, or into an insipid body, etc.) those, above all, will be worth your noting, being the most luciferous, and many times luciferous, and many times luciferous experiments too in philosophy.

"As for particulars, these that follow are all that I can now think of viz., Whether at Schemnitium, in Hungary, (where there are mines of gold, copper, iron, vitriol, antimony, etc.) they change iron into copper by dissolving it in a vitriolate water, which they find in cavitys of rocks in the mines, and then melting the slimy solution in a strong fire, which in the cooling proves copper. The like is said to be done in other places, which I can not now remember; perhaps, too, it may be done in Italy. For about twenty or thirty years agone there was a certain vitrioll came from thence, (called Roman vitrioll,) but of a nobler virtue than that which is now called by that name; which vitrioll is not now to be gotten, because, perhaps, they make a greater gain by some such trick as turning iron into copper with it, than by selling it. 2. Whether in Hungary, Sclavonia, Bohemia,

[231]

near the town Eila, or at the mountains of Bohemia near Silesia, there be rivers whose waters are impregnated with gold; perhaps, the gold being dissolved by some corrosive waters like *aqua regia*, and the solution carried along with the streame, that runs through the mines, till it be tinged with gold, and then straining the mercury through leather, that the gold may stay behind, be a secret yet, or openly practised. 3. There is newly contrived, in Holland, a mill to grind glasses plane withall, and I think polishing them too; perhaps it will be worth the while to see it. 4. There is in Holland one ———— Borry, who some years since was imprisoned by the Pope, to have extorted from him secrets (as I am told) of great worth, both as to medicine and profit, but he escaped into Holland, where they have granted him a guard. I think he usually goes cloathed in green. Pray inquire what you can of him, and whether his ingenuity be any profit to the Dutch."

At the time this letter was written (1669) Newton was very busy with the construction of his reflecting telescope, and was doing experiments on the alloys of certain metals. In a letter written a little later (1671–72) he mentions the general results of these experiments, "which to a great extent have been the guide of all who have followed him in the construction of metallic specula for reflecting telescopes.'' In addition to the letter he has left a full account of the composition of his specula, and of the method of founding them, in a paper written in his own hand, and entitled *De Metallo ad conficiendum speculum componendo et fundendo.*[3]

A second source of evidence that Newton was deeply interested in alchemy is his letters to and from Boyle and Locke. The correspondence extended over a long period and can not be considered systematically. Nevertheless we can present a typical example. Before doing so, however, we ought to emphasize one essential historical fact.

''In Boyle's time, chemistry was chiefly in the hands of three kinds of men: first, those who used its operations in order to prepare remedies and nostrums—the pharmacologists of that day; second, those who sought to create gold—the alchymists proper; third, the schoolmen, who sought (or claimed to possess) a theory of matter. Naturally, the drug-makers, the gold-makers, and the theory-makers were not sharply distinct, and a single practitioner could unite all three interests.''[4]

Newton, Boyle, and Locke were in the second and third classes. But they were really philosophers—not alchemists nor speculators in the popular sense. They were not seeking wealth, health,

[3] Brewster II, App. No. XXXI, p. 535.
[4] Masson's *Three Centuries of Chemistry*, p. 57.

and long life. In their experiments and speculations about matter they were prompted by "a love of truth, a desire to make new discoveries in chemistry, and a wish to test the extraordinary pretensions of their predecessors and their contemporaries." As far as Newton's experiments and inquiries were limited to the transmutation and multiplication of metals, we must conclude that he was seeking an underlying principle which would justify the announcement of a generalization in chemistry. His progress was painfully slow, his methods were sadly inferior to those he used in other fields, and he completely failed to find any trace of a principle; nevertheless his motive was the motive of a philosopher not of a financier, physician, or fanatic.

Let us return to Newton, Boyle and Locke's participation in "multiplying gold." We can summarize (by quoting) what Brewster says:[5]

"While Newton was corresponding with Locke in 1692, the process of Boyle for 'multiplying gold,' by combining a certain red earth with mercury, became the subject of discussion Mr. Boyle having 'left the inspection of his papers' to Locke, Dr Dickison, and Dr. Cox, Mr. Locke became acquainted with the particulars of the process we have referred to. Boyle had, before his

[5] Vol. II, p. 120.

death, communicated this process both to Locke and Newton, and procured some of the red earth for his friends. Having received some of this earth from Locke, Newton tells him, that though he has 'no inclination to prosecute the process,' yet, as he had 'a mind to prosecute it,' he would 'be glad to assist him,' though 'he feared he had lost the first and third of the process out of this pocket.' He goes on to thank Locke for 'what he communicated to him out of his own notes about it,' and adds in a postscript, that 'when the hot weather is over, he intends to try the beginning (that is the first of the three parts of the recipe,) though the success seems improbable.'"[6]

In Locke's answer of July 26, he sends to Newton a transcript of two of Boyle's papers, as he knew he wished it; and, it is obvious from their letters, that both of them were desirous of "multiplying gold." In Newton's very interesting reply to this communication, he "dissuades Locke against incurring any expense by a too hasty trial of the recipe." He says, that several chemists were engaged in trying the process, and that Mr. Boyle, in communicating it to himself, "had reserved a part of it from my knowledge, though I knew more of it than he has told me." This

[6] This letter, of which there is only a fragment, is dated Cambridge, July 7 1692, and is published in Edleston's *Correspondence*.

mystery on the part of Boyle is very remarkable. In "offering his secret" to Newton and Locke, he imposed conditions upon them, while in the case of Newton at least, he did not perform his own part in the arrangement. On another occasion, when he communicated two experiments in return for one, "he cumbered them," says Newton, "with such circumstances as startled me and made me afraid of any more." It is a curious fact, as appears from this letter, that there was then a Company established in London to multiply gold by this receipe, which Newton "takes to be the thing for the sake of which Mr. Boyle procured the repeal of the Art of Parliament against multipliers."

Although Boyle had possessed this golden receipe for twenty years, yet Newton could not find that he had "either tried it himself, or got it tried successfully by any body else; "for," he says, "when I spoke doubtingly about it, he confessed that he had not seen it tried, but added that a certain gentleman was now about it, and it succeeded very well so far as he had gone, and that all the signs appeared, so that I needed not doubt of it." From this rather long summary it is evident that we have merely a repetition of the "same old story"—someone had seen or heard that gold was produced, but no one had the gold.

It would not be profitable to pursue this type of

evidence any farther, because as far as I can discover only one significant fact is revealed by the
correspondence between Newton and his contemporaries, viz., their interest in alchemy and
their pursuit of it by aimless experiments yielded
no results that convinced these men that their
beliefs were true.

Another line of evidence shows that Newton
studied a large number of books on alchemy. Some
of these books are annotated. His papers, many
of which are still in existence (in the Portsmouth
Collection), also contain extended extracts from
books by well-known alchemists. These evidences
are said by some authorities to prove that Newton
was a firm believer in alchemy. I am rather
inclined to conclude that they show diligence in
the search for an underlying philosophical principle
rather than belief in the unproved principle.
They point to an experimental philosopher rather
than a busy alchemist. However, there is not
the slightest doubt as to his interest and labors,
whatever his belief. I cite some of the books. There
were found among Newton's papers copious extracts
from Jacob Behmen's works in his own handwriting. There were also found in Newton's handwriting, *The Metamorphoses of the Planets*, by John
De Monte Snyders, in 62 pages, 4to, and a key to
the same work, and numerous pages of alchemist

poetry from Norton's *Ordinal*, and Basil Valentine's *Mystery of the Microcosm*. There was likewise found a copy of *Secrets Revealed, or an open entrance to the Shut Palace of the King*, which is covered with notes in Newton's handwriting, in which great changes are made in the language and meaning of the thirty-five chapters of which it consists. There was also found a beautifully written, but incomplete copy of William Yarworth's *Processus Mysterii Magni Philosophicus*, and also a small manuscript in his handwriting, entitled *Thesaurus Thesaurorum sive Medicina Aurea*.

We should recall in this connection that from his earliest days Newton was in the habit of copying extracts from various sources, often without apparent reason, thinking perhaps, as most scholars do, that he might sometime find a use for the material. I do not know the date when these extracts, annotations, and copies were made, but it is a fact that Newton often threw himself into protracted periods of deep study. One of these periods came soon after his mother's death. He plunged into theological study, and conducted a voluminous correspondence on mathematical subjects. It was at this time, according to a reliable authority, that "he gave free rein to his lifelong interest in alchemy, and studied many old and contemporary books on this subject [and] interested himself in a method due to Boyle for making gold out of mercury.'' Perhaps the deep alchemical studies were pursued at this time.

One of the best sources of evidence of Newton's interest and work in alchemy is the *Portsmouth Collection of Books and Papers Written by or Belonging to Sir Isaac Newton.*

After Newton's death many of his books and papers came into the possession of John Conduitt, who had married Catharine Barton, Newton's step-niece. Through this marriage the books and papers eventually became the property of Lord Portsmouth at Hurstbourne. They were inspected by Horsley when preparing his edition of Newton's works, but largely ignored. Later the collection was examined by Brewster, who made some use of it in his *Life of Newton.*

In 1872 the Earl of Portsmouth turned over the *Collection* to the University of Cambridge, with a request that it be examined and all papers on theology, chronology, history, and alchemy, as well as those relating to private, personal, and family matters be returned to him. The University appointed a syndicate to examine, classify, and divide the collection. This was done, and a report was prepared, which was printed as *A Catalogue of the Portsmouth Collection of Books and Papers written by or belonging to Sir Isaac Newton, the*

Scientific Portion of which has been presented by the Earl of Portsmouth to the University of Cambridge (Cambridge, 1888).

A copy of this Report is in the Boston Public Library and I have examined it carefully several times. As a whole the chemistry portion is disappointing because of the meagre references. On the other hand, the starred titles indicate that many of these papers were returned by the University to the Earl of Portsmouth and no doubt these and perhaps some of the others would prove to be fruitful if examined by a small group of chemists who are informed about the alchemists noted in the items and who are also familiar with the chemistry of Newton's time. The syndicate did not seem to have a high estimate of these papers, judging by this part of the Preface to their Report:

"Newton's manuscripts on Alchemy are of very little interest in themselves. He seems to have made transcripts from a variety of authors, and, if we may judge by the number of praxes of their contents which he began and left unfinished, he seems to have striven in vain to trace a connected system in the processes described. He has left, however, notes of a number of his own chemical experiments made at various dates between 1678 and 1696. Some of these are quantitative. Those of most interest relate to alloys. He mentions

[240]

several easily fusible alloys of bismuth, tin and lead, and gives as the most fusible that which contains 5 parts of lead + 7 of tin + 12 of bismuth. He says that an alloy consisting of 2 parts of lead + 3 of tin + 4 of bismuth will melt in the sun in the summer. The alloy which goes by his name is in the proportions of either of these two; but as he states that tinglas (bismuth) is more fusible than tin, he could not have used pure metal. The note-book which contains the longest record of his chemical experiments contains also the account of a few optical and other physics experiments and the paper on the decussation of the optic nerve published by Harris and from him by Brewster.''

The chemistry part is in Section II, pages 11 to 24. It consists largely of titles and very brief abstracts, though the part designated *VI A Manuscript Notebook* contains longer extracts from designated pages. It should be noted at the outset that the *Portsmouth Collection* as far as chemistry and alchemy are concerned consists almost entirely of titles or of very brief abstracts. We do not know what the balance is nor have we any data for an appraisal. The year of its examination, 1872, was a long time ago from the stand-point of values in historical chemistry. Who knows what it might not yield upon adequate re-examination? In any case it should be more fully published as a contribution to the history of chemistry.

As stated in the preface of the *Collection* the chemistry section consists mainly of an itemized account by titles and very brief abstracts of "five parcels containing transcripts from various alchemical authors in Newton's handwriting, with notes and abstracts." These items are too fragmentary and disconnected to warrant reproduction in this paper. Divisions I to V contain in all about 180 items. The manuscript note-book is 283 pages, though only a portion of the items is mentioned.

Some items from Divisions I to V have historical value. There are nine extracts from Lully, five from Valentine (including one to the *Triumphal Car of Antimony*), nine from Ripley, three from Flamel, two from van Helmont, and one each from Mynsicht, Norton, Dickenson, Geber, Spagretus, and Yarworth. Of the last named, two copies of his *Processus Mysterii Magni Philosophicus* are mentioned. Of books or extracts specifically mentioning alchemy there are seven, including one set of forty-seven alchemical recipes and a manuscript book on alchemy (author not given) dated 1610. Direct references to transmutation and the philosopher's stone are eight, including a diagram of the philosopher's stone and a packet marked "Medicine to transmute copper." There are three items concerning hieroglyphics. Section IV contains eleven items covering "notes on experiments all in Newton's handwriting."

As examples of the kind of items in I to III in the Collection, I select the following:

"8. Basil Valentine: on the minerals of Hungary, Carinthia, etc., and the conditions of their formation, and on the transmutation of metals and the separation of the three principals and of vitriol.

Jodochus a Rehe: processes for preparing the Philosopher's stone from MSS. in possession of Dr. Twysden. Copies of 4 letters from Faber to Dr. Twysden, 1673–4, recounting success of experiments in preparing spirits of mercury. Notes on Faber's work.

23. Account of furnaces, etc.

24. Extracts from Flamel and several other authors.

7. An alchemical recipe headed 'Roth Mallor's work.' On the back of the folio a recipe for making *aqua regia* from calcium chloride and aqua fortis, and for another menstruum which seems to be a solution of antimony chloride, the Second Period (a part of the foregoing recipe), but not in Newton's hand.

8. Notes of reference to some alchemical works. Diagrams of furnaces. Two recipes for making clay

for furnaces and lutes. Note that 'for rectifying spirits and ethereal oyles, nothing is better than the bladder of an ox or hogg,' and a recipe for calcining gold which seems only getting it into a fine powder.

9. Dr. Goddard's experiments of refining gold with antimony extracted from *Phil. Trans.*

10. Part of a letter ordering someone to procure for Newton from Hamburg various metallic ores.

11. Notes of stannic chloride, and some chemical reactions.

12. An alchemical experiment, not in Newton's hand, which seems part of some larger work. There is a note in Newton's hand on it relating to quantities obtained in some distillation."

In Division IV the items are dated and give us a helpful glimpse of the character of Newton's experiments from 1678 to 1695. I include all the items.

"*IV. Notes on Experiments, all in Newton's Hand.*

1. Dec. 10, 1678 to Jan. 15. Subliming antimony with salammoniac. Alloying antimony with lead and other metals. (No definite result of value.)

2. Jan. 1679–80. Subliming antimonial sublimate with lead antimoniate, etc. Jan. 22. Action

of nitric acid and salammoniac on antimony sulphide, heat and further sublimations. (Most of these experiments are roughly quantitative.)

3. Feb. 1679–80. Fusing antimony with vitriol and other things. Sublimation of various metals by help of antimony and salammoniac, etc. Action of oil of vitriol on galena, of nitric acid on sublimate of antimony, and others of a like kind.

4. August 1682. Similar experiments; some on lead ore, others on an alloy of tin and bismuth which he seems to call Diana.

5. July 10 (no year), 'vidi-philosophicum.' Sublimations of calx albus with salammoniac.

6. April 26, 1686. On a volatile salt of zinc (apparently the chloride), and on an alloy derived from ores of iron, antimony, tin, lead, and bismuth. May 16. 'On ven. vol.'

7. March 5, 1690–1 and March 16. On some bismuth components and the action of aqua fortis on alloys of tin and bismuth and zinc.

8. Experiments and observations. Dec. 1692 and Jan. 1692–3. Working of barm. He says 'in distilling new wine before fermentation, the flegm rises first, and then the spirit, but after fermentation, the spirit rises before the flegm.' Other experiments. Comparison of the fusibility of alloys of lead, tin, and bismuth, in which is given as the most fusible an alloy of 5 of lead

+ 7 of tin + 12 of bismuth. April 1693 and June 1693, further experiments.

9. April, 1695, experiments with antimony and ores of iron, copper and tin and sublimations with salammoniac. Feb. 1695–6, sublimations of antimony with iron ore.

    10. Notes of Chemical Experiments, without date:

        Action of aqua fortis on antimony sulphide, etc.

        Sublimation of alloy of antimony and lead with salammoniac, etc.

        Experiments on lead ore and other things.

        Do. on copper, etc.

        Other experiments.

    11. *De metallo ad confinendum speculum componendo et fundendo.* Printed by Brewster, ii, 535.''

Division V is a miscellaneous collection dealing mainly with gems, though it contains a copy of *De Natura Acidorum.* I include it merely for reference and completeness.

"V. Miscellaneous Notes

    1. Notes on Magnetism. It does not appear whence they are taken. The observations (some of which are erroneous) do not seem to be Newton's, though here and there remarks upon them seem to be his.

[246]

2. De Natura Acidorum, with a copy. This is printed in Horsley's *Newton*, iv, pp. 397–400.

3. 11 points for enquiry in Physics.

4. *De Gemmis in genere*, mostly from Berquen, Boethius, Tavernier, and Boyle. Index of refraction in diamonds is given 41/100 on the authority of Halley. On page 3 is mentioned a very fragile and soft western Topaz which he found to have a sp. gr. 4.27, though the sines of refraction were as 14 to 23 (could this be Baryte?) On page 7 he deducts from the cleavage that gems are crystallized like salts from juices which turn to stone. At the end are the gold and silver standards of different countries.

5. De Gemmis. Other notes mostly included in the preceding, but on page 1 are given reasons for thinking the diamond coagulated from a fluid and fat substance, which he does not seem to have incorporated in the preceding.

6. Of Gemms. Part of the foregoing in English.

7. Extracts from Berquen.

8. Order notes on gems.

9. Gemmarum pretia.''

The manuscript notebook has 283 pages and consists of notes on experiments together with extracts from Boyle's writings. The items are tantalizingly brief. I cite some of the most interesting.

[247]

"VI. A Manuscript Note-book.

p. 50, account of experiments on flame—with conclusion that flame and vapour differ only as bodies red-hot and not red-hot.

p. 65, extracts from Starkey's Pyrotechny asserted.

p. 80, experiments on the extraction of mercury from the nitrate and from corrosive sublimate by various other metals.

pp. 81, 82, receipts for making regulus of antimony by different metals.

p. 83, notes of alloys which fuse at low temperatures, others which give a crystalline mass from fusion. Notes of the action of aquafortis, and of salammoniac, on salt, and oil of tartar or potassium carbonate; and of crude tartar on the same, and of tartarum vitriolatum (potassium bicarbonate) on same: with

p. 84, the remark that some Fools call the result of the last reaction magisterium tartar of vitriolati.

Note, that salammoniac is less volatile than muriatic acid or ammonium carbonate, which seems to explain a quotation from D. von der Becke which follows.

Note of calcination of lead with salt of antimony and salammoniac and of volatilization of arsenical tin when heated with corrosive sublimate and salammoniac.

p. 101, receipts for making sundry preparations of antimony. Note of the action of corrosive sublimate on various ores.

p. 102, notes on experiments in the preparation of regulus of antimony.

p. 103, do, and of action of corrosive sublimate on antimony, silver and mercury; of the heat produced by mixing oil of vitriol with water or spirit of wine; of the preparation of ether and oil of wine—not differing much from the account quoted on p. 64.

p. 104, 105, note of warmth on mixing water with spirit of antimony, and of secondary chemical reactions—the last on saturation of spirit of antimony by different substances as blanks left for the quantities.

p. 106, 107, other chemical experiments. Note of composition of fusible metal 'which in summer will melt in the sun' with the (erroneous) remark that tinglas is more fusible than tin.

p. 108–112, chemical experiments chiefly on preparations of antimony and scoria of regulus. Some of these (e.g. p. 111) are marked with an N in the margin.

p. 113, action of distilled liquor of antimony on salts of lead, iron, and copper; action of heat on tartarized antimony.

p. 114, action of spar on distilled liquor of

antimony, vinegar, and aquafortis, and of salt from clay of lead mines on do.; action of nitre on antimony.

p. 115, 116, action of oil of vitriol on lead ore, and of an antimonial sublimate on several substances.

pp. 123 sqq. to 126, account of experiments in May and June 1682; on sublimation of some salts with salammoniac, and some metals and alloys with the same, and with antimony.

pp. 135 sqq., Feb. 29, 1683–4. An experiment in which he prepared the chlorides of mercury.

pp. 140 sqq., further experiments on "the net" which seems to contain iron and copper, and others of a similar kind. On page 149 is the date February, May 23.

p. 150, experiments on the spirit of zinc, April 26, 1686.

p. 151 to 158, experiments on some alloys of copper, antimony, and iron, and continued on p. 267.

p. 209–223, extracts from Starkey's Pyrotechny asserted—on alkalies.

p. 267, 268, continuation of experiments from p. 158. On this page is mentioned a liquor which dissolves the tinctures out of gold, silver, etc., and leaves only a white calx—but no directions of preparing it. Further experiments.

[250]

pp. 269–283, on regulus of antimony and alloys; similar in character to the former; rest of book blank, except three pages at end, where is a list of prices of some chemicals in 1687 and again in 1693, and some notes of sublimation of vitriol with salammoniac.''

It is regrettable that students of the history of chemistry have not been able to study this note book. Perhaps some learned society will publish it *in extenso* in the near future.

Another source of evidence which would show Newton's deep and continuous interest in alchemy is certain books from his library. He says frequently that he took books from the University library. But he must have had a library of his own for we know from bills and records that he bought books on alchemy. Yet it seems strange that none of his biographers refers to his library. Brewster mentions some of the books which Newton bought, and others which were presented to him, but without giving a clue to their disposal or fate. The *Portsmouth Collection* contains only a few books. Hence, we might properly ask: What became of Newton's books? Were they destroyed, given to individuals, dispersed without their ownership being made known, and thus lost to posterity?

The mystery enshrouding Newton's library was

not unveiled till 1920 and then only partly. We are indebted to H. Zeitlinger for the facts. He says in part:

"On January 13th to 15th, 1920, there was an auction sale in England at Thame Park, Oxon., of *The Greater Portion of the Contents of the Mansion, early 19th Century English Furniture of excellent workmanship*, . . . etc. etc. etc., *and* (in small type) *Books*. The books formed less than thirty lots, some of them being bundled up, after the manner of book-auctioneers, in lots of 40, 120, and even 200 volumes. There was nothing to indicate their importance except this, that five books are specifically mentioned 'with the Autograph of Isaac Newton.'

"One of the most interesting books in the collection was the presentation copy from the author to Newton of Huygens's *Horologium Oscillatorium*. There was also the *Theatrum Chemicum*, 1659–61 (6 vols.), of which Brewster relates that Newton purchased it in April, 1669, for £1 8s. 6d. It is full of notes in his handwriting, as are also many of the other alchemical books in the same collection. These notes are of importance mainly in showing that Newton was interested in the mystic element of alchemy. Several of the books were by Robert Boyle, and contained either his presentation inscription to Newton, or a note by the latter, stating that they were given to him. Nearly all were bound in a late Seventeeth or early Eighteenth Century English calf, and were, almost without exception, in remarkably good preservation. Many showed signs of use by having both top and bottom corners turned in Newton's peculiar manner, and it must be confessed that this happened in most cases in works on theology and alchemy. . . .

"For some years after the sale, books from this collection could be seen in the catalogues of many of the London second-hand book-sellers, some with inscriptions by or to Newton, but alas! without any reference to MS. notes by him. A few found their way into the sale rooms, and only after the sale were they found to contain Newton's notes."

A recent catalogue of an English dealer in second-hand books contains a list of twenty books "from Sir Isaac Newton's Library." Six of these books are on alchemy. One is by Zacharias Brendel, dealing with the preparation of potable gold; it was published in 1630 and has Newton's bookplate with the motto "Philosophemur." Another is by Christoph Glaser—*Traité de la Chymie;* it was published in 1676, and also has the bookplate. Another is the *Opera Mineralia* of Isaacus Hollandus; it was published in 1600, has the bookplate, with the motto, "and," the catalogue says, "a number of corners turned down in Newton's characteristic bad manner." Another is William Johnson's *Lexicon Chymicum*, 1678. An important item is a "bound up" copy of a book by Lullius and one by Alsted, 1609. The titles are long, the bookplate is present, and there is a Greek quotation in Newton's handwriting on the title page. And finally there is one by Johann Schröder dealing with pharmaceutical and medical operations, published in 1679, and having the bookplate.

We also know Newton owned one of John Dee's books and one of Geber's; the latter contains copious notes in Newton's handwriting. Reference has already been made in this paper to a "theatrium chemicum" bought by Newton and to certain other alchemical books owned and annotated by him.

Unfortunately for students of Newton's work in alchemy most of these books are not available. They are in public libraries, a few museums, and scattered among private libraries. An examination of these books annotated by Newton would yield much new information about his studies and experiments in alchemy.

Newton was elected President of the Royal Society in 1703, and was thus honored for his unbroken interest in the Society since 1672 and at last rewarded for his brilliant contributions to science. As President he fostered the work of the

Society in all its departments. He must have retained his interest in chemistry for we know that as President he gave his "imprimatur" to Hales *Vegetable Staticks* in 1727. This is probably the last book to which Newton affixed his title for this purpose (*i.e.*, the "imprimatur"). He carried on his functions as President till the very end of his life, indeed his last official act was to preside at a meeting of the Royal Society on March 2, 1727, (only eighteen days before his death).

In conclusion let me point out again that although Newton did many chemical and alchemical experiments continuously for about thirty-five years (1661–1696) in his laboratory beside the great gate of Trinity College at Cambridge, his chief purpose does not seeem to have been the transmutation of base metals into fine gold but rather a diligent search for a great principle which would transform disconnected chemical phenomena into a philosophical system.

NEWTON'S PLACE IN THE HISTORY OF RELIGIOUS THOUGHT

tions to science: perhaps his famous words were the expression of a life-long sentiment and he really felt at all times that he was, to use his famous metaphor, playing beside a mighty ocean and living for a brief time on the shores of "that immortal sea that brought us hither." At least this much is certain, that in bulk Newton's theological writings are as big as his scientific writings, that his interest was keen, and that he felt no shadow of doubt about the importance of the subjects he undertook to elucidate.

The subjects included two particular passages of the New Testament, the Prophecies of Daniel and the Apocalypse of John, and the general principles of religion and church government. In dealing with two texts (I JOHN ii.7 and I TIMOTHY iii.16) Newton appears in the capacity of higher critic. It is difficult to say whether Newton was inspired by a love of accuracy or a particular doctrinal interest. Personally I suspect that mathematical accuracy was the ruling motive, but it was unfortunate that in both cases Newton supported corrections and interpretations which were anti-Trinitarian. The result was likely to be embarassing. Newton always disliked the publicity which a dispute involves: he had enough troubles with what he called "the litigious lady," philosophy. Those were uncertain times: the Toleration Act of 1688 had specially named among those not protected by its formula all writers against the Trinity and the great Whiston was actually expelled from Cambridge in 1711 for the sin of Arianism. Newton therefore took every precaution to conceal the authorship of the critical emendations. The letters which contained them were given to John Locke to be copied and then sent to Le Clerc in Holland for publication. So much toil and trouble would hardly have been faced if Newton had not felt that in this work he was doing something important for the progress of religion.

The work entitled *Observations upon the Prophecies of Daniel and the Apocalypse of John* must have had its origin in two different interests. The fact of prophecy and the significance of the apocalyptic language were accepted as axioms: this was the faith that went in search of understanding. Also Newton was notoriously susceptible to the challenge of a problem: it was only necessary to present him with a difficult question in order to bring all his faculties into action. The apocalyptic writings were astronomical puzzles. Through all the ages since the Babylonian captivity there had been a continual stream of thought that reflected the starry heavens and seemed to be a mirror of eternity. The astronomical symbolism attracted

[261]

Newton: the books seemed to him examples of a method as symbolic as the mathematical: it was only necessary to say "let the sun equal the whole race of Kings" or "let the moon equal the common people" and the equations would work out with infallible accuracy. As Sir David Brewster tells us, Newton did not look for the secrets of the future and confound prophecy with necromancy: a prophecy was an anticipation which became intelligible after it had been fulfilled and then would "afford convincing argument that the world is governed by Providence." This very laborious and detailed treatise has been published recently in a form that is intended to make it acceptable to the general public. Whether the interpretation of these prophecies has any value I am not competent to say: along with the majority of the general public I have failed to read the work: allowing that all prophecies must be fulfilled sooner or later, I have found no proof of the initial assumption made by Newton, namely that they had already been fulfilled sufficiently to be interpreted.

This seems the right place to note the fact that some people ascribe all Newton's theological interests to a temporary loss of mental power. Such a view is interesting because it draws attention to the fact that there is a class of persons who argue that a religious or theological interest is in itself adequate proof of mental degeneration. In Newton's case some plausibility was given to the argument by asserting that the death of his mother in 1690 was the event that created his religious enthusiasm and produced both the theological writings and the supposed mental trouble of 1693. But as there is enough evidence to show that some of the writings are earlier than 1690 and in any case the illness of 1693 could not properly be called insanity, the matter is not worth further consideration. The truth is that Newton was not a Newtonian. The Newtonians in the century after the master's death went so far in their exaggeration of his principles that they could not even understand how Newton himself was able to reconcile science and religion. But the logical attitude of Newton and his freedom from fanaticism are well shown in the minor works and tracts left for publication by Sir Isaac Newton's niece (Mrs. Conduitt). Here we see Newton thinking for himself with natural simplicity and directness. In reference to the great controversy about the word "homoousios" he asks, "Whether Christ sent his apostles to preach metaphysics to the unlearned common people and to their wives and children?" A very pertinent question! As he grew older Newton grew fonder of drawing up concise epitomes of religion, as though he hoped to state the axiomatic principles from which all future religion could be deduced. In ecclesiastical politics he lays down the principle that "the laws of the King extend only to things that are left indifferent and undetermined by the laws of God." So in his special work on religious questions we see in Newton a critic of texts, a learned expositor, a liberal thinker and a faithful son of the Church as constituted by the laws of God.

Though honor has been done in the nineteenth century to Newton's ability as a critic and admirers have resuscitated his views on the Apocalypse, far greater importance must be attached to the general effect which his work had on the current of British and European thought. This effect was not accidental nor was it produced by mere force of suggestion. The Boyle Lectureship had been founded to provide proofs of the existence of God by arguments drawn from Nature, and Dr. Bentley was appointed to lecture in 1692. Bentley wisely decided to lean upon Newton and the resulting correspondence drew from Newton some explicit applications of his theory to the question of divine creation and control. The second edition of the *Principia* contains a declaration of faith which may be regarded as the most complete and most exact statement which Newton gave of his beliefs. In the language of Colin MacLaurin, who represents the cultured opinion of Newton's time, "Sir Isaac Newton infers from the structure of the visible world that it is governed by the Almighty and All-wise Being, who rules the world not as its Soul but as its Lord, exercising an absolute sovereignty over the universe, not as over his own body but as over his work." On the next page Colin MacLaurin gives us a valuable hint as to what was in the air. He refers to the New Platonists as authors of "the most mystical and unintelligible notions concerning the Deity;" indicating that Newton's good sense had delivered science from all such evils. And in point of fact Newton had done this, or rather he had completed the process; but the proper understanding of this topic calls for a brief retrospect.

From very early times, and more particularly the second century of the Christian era there had grown up a close connexion between the idea of light and the idea of the Kingdom of God. As an all-pervading, motionless and very pure substance light was eminently qualified to be the dwelling-place of God: also it was declared to be the "matter" which formed the body of the resurrection. Accordingly we find the nature of light is a subject that stimulates curiosity, a fearful wonder half scientific and half metaphysical. From Roger Bacon to Laplace we trace the same complex interest and the same ambiguity in "celestial" subjects. That the uttermost limit of space was the threshold of the house of God remained a conviction of the human mind in spite of such enlightened heretics as Giordano Bruno, in spite of the defection of Kepler, in spite even of the work of Galileo and Newton. But as light became more and more reducible to simple laws and formulae, as the idea of motionless colourless purity passed away when the movement was measured and the colours produced by the prism, the pantheism that diffused Deity through the transparent medium of light was deprived of its main support. For those pantheists God was an indwelling Reason, the law and the nature of things. But in the age of Newton the sciences demanded a law of a different kind, a formula not a Logos, a mathematical calculation not an incarnate Deity. If Nature was ruled by an indwelling spirit there must be left some scope for animism, some incalculable "act of God:" the logical course for the scientist is always to "deanimate nature." Then the act of God becomes one and one only—namely the original act of Creation. God, according to Newton, is not reason but will: he is not the soul of the world but the Lord of All. Religion and science are then reconciled, provided that religion accepts an inactive Deity and science, as Laplace said "requires no such hypothesis." But discontent was apparent on both sides. Newton found his cosmology must either be limited to phenomena and formulae or be extended to include the acts of God. It was not the custom of the age to accept limits: if a man did not employ God he might be said to have dismissed him. Under this influence we see Newton reconsidering the metaphysical completeness of his formulae and assigning important operations to God. Fate could never produce the regularity we see in nature; this must be due to God, the irregularities being apparently due to opposing forces. Also the unity of all things seems desirable but it is not easy to conceive it: if God as a thinking Being were regarded as viewing all things at one time, these things passing as it were before his sensorium, the unity would be provided for: and this was Newton's explanation of it. But, in spite of these important possibilities, it is clear that God was slowly being converted into the order of nature: time, space and unity were really the indispensable factors which seemed to compel science to keep God in the Universe. And when the word has been uttered and God is enthroned, nothing more can be done. The world is a machine, its movements and changes are all a shifting and disposition of parts reducible to analytical formulae and expressible (at last) in the language of the calculus or fluxions. Newton's followers rightly took from the Master the hint to go their ways untroubled by any fear of the act of God and unmoved by the possibility of miracles. The proper conclusion of Newtonism is deism and the deists deserve credit for having faced the issue.

The influence of Newton is most clearly seen in the attempts to restate the moral laws in terms of exact mathematical deduction. In the history of religion there has always been an influence which is loosely called Platonism. The mathematical basis of Platonism is shown in the belief that Divine Government is made known to men by a universal order which can be translated into mathematical or geometrical terms. Religion can therefore be demonstrated as well as believed. The Platonist holds that the recognition of eternal truth is achieved by an innate power: there is a revelation from within. When this is made inarticulate and akin to feeling, it becomes a form of mysticism or of pietism. When this inner faculty is considered to be reason, the theory is a form of intellectualism. The outstanding representative of this doctrine was Samuel Clarke who derived his inspiration from Newton and proceeded to construct a theory of natural relations from which all rules of conduct could be deduced. Clarke was a

Boyle lecturer and imitated the others in his zeal to unite the idea of God with the idea of cosmic reason. This plan requires us to learn the natural or objective order of the Universe before we can arrive at the truth about the Divine Nature. In this way a severe rationalism was put forward in opposition to all the romantic forms of religion that went by the name of "enthusiasm." The seat of religious belief was thus moved from the heart to the head: mysticism was excommunicated by mathematics. Locke exposed his Newtonism when he said that ethics could be demonstrated; and his critic remarked that Locke only said he would like to see it done, not that he proposed to do it. Because the rules of conduct could be deduced from relations (as for example obedience from the relation of the child to the parent) and relations were clearer than any other doctrines, religion was put on its trial and ultimately found wanting. The theological argument was now reversed and intellect was made the judge over faith. Goodness was considered a self-evident truth from which the goodness of God could be inferred. Since this implied the criticism of revelation by reason and the substitution of individual enquiry for authority, the way was opened for a liberal Christianity which might ultimately supersede traditional beliefs. It is not surprising that the outcome of this movement

[269]

should be a "religion within the limits of reason."
That was the phrase chosen by Kant to express
his own view, and Kant was in this respect as in
many others the logical conclusion of the movements fostered by the eighteenth century. But
Kant also dominated the opening of the nineteenth
century and in his work is seen the triumph of the
Newtonian method. Religion is to be based upon
morality: morality is part of the order of nature
and based upon the laws of nature: the work of
reason is the only sure foundation on which to
build a living creed and save mankind from the
domination of superstition. This was nowhere
stated by Newton, but it was the inevitable outcome of the particular scientific ideals which
originated from his work. The eighteenth century
elaborated the idea of the Newtonian world-
machine. The idea was lofty and served its
purpose: the age subscribed to the formula "Order
is God's first law."

This idea of law became so dominant that there
was no longer any room for creative activity. The
union between law and necessity grew up almost
unperceived and was accepted as indisputable
truth: libertarians and necessitarians fought a
hopeless battle with no alternatives except fate
and freewill. Only a radical change in the basis of
calculations could liberate the disputants from this

hopeless situation, and that change was initiated
by the rise of biological interests. This did not
mean the rejection of law in nature but a new conception of the relation between law and creative
power. From the consideration of evolution, the
characteristic novelty of the nineteenth century
and the special mark which distinguishes it from
the eighteenth, there has arisen a new conception
of the origin and value of physical laws. They
can now be understood as instruments which the
mind of man produces in the course of mental
evolution to assist him in the solution of his
problem of adaptation. They are not on that
account less true or less real but they are more
vitally related to man's existence. The Newtonian
world-machine was a device for the simplification
of scientific problems. Newton himself would
have agreed with the modern view, if that particular aspect of the question had been presented
to him. Some writers have referred with gentle
sarcasm to the functions of God in Newton's work,
as if Newton thought the Deity to be concerned
only in supplying the gaps of a defective cosmology. But it is truer to the facts to see in Newton's language the confession that knowledge has
its limits and beyond those limits there can only
be faith that asserts Divine action. Science was
for Newton the part of theology which could be

[271]

reduced to demonstrative form. As another scientific thinker has recently said "Science is the highest form of reasoning about God." Beyond a doubt that was Newton's own belief and, in spite of bigotry and superstition, that belief continues to spread among mankind.

The conclusion of the argument is that Newton affected the progress of religious thought in two different ways. He contributed certain special writings to the literature of theology. But in a far deeper way he affected religious thought by destroying the ancient tradition of the two worlds, celestial and terrestrial, and establishing the idea of law in the Universe as one and the same throughout. This led to a form of thought which at first seemed detrimental to religion but was in fact a process of purification through which men learned that the idea of God and the idea of law are not antagonistic. Since that period the work which Newton began has continued to grow and at the present time it influences the world; for every day men are learning that worship of the Creator is more than a sabbatic ritual: it is essentially a spirit of discovery and an effort to direct desire by knowledge. Newton so far surpassed the average man in his power to comprehend Nature and give her laws expression that his final convictions are of more than ordinary interest. A restatement of his views will serve to remind this generation that he found in Nature what seemed to him indisputable signs, if not actual proofs, of the skill and wisdom of a Creator.

NEWTON IN THE MINT

NEWTON IN THE MINT

GEORGE E. ROBERTS

Vice President of the National City Bank of New York and former Director of the United States Mint

S IR ISAAC NEWTON was Lucasian professor of mathematics at Cambridge when, in March, 1696, he was appointed Warden of the British Mint. The appointment came at the half-way point of his adult life. He had spent thirty-one years in the university life at Cambridge after graduation, and there followed thirty-one years in London as an official of the Mint, to his death in 1727.

His appointment at the Mint was so eminently fitting that it almost seems out of place to mention that it had any relation to politics, but apparently politics was a factor in it. The Mint positions were political places, and Macaulay says that the office of Warden to which Newton was first appointed, "had become a mere sinecure, and had been filled by a succession of fine gentlemen who were well known at the hazard table of Whitehall but who never condescended to come near the Tower"—where the Mint was located.

Newton, of course, was not a political hanger-on, or that type of an office holder, but he was a member of the Whig party then, and had represented the University of Cambridge in the so-called Convention Parliament which met at Westminster early in 1680 and formally established William of Orange and his wife Mary, daughter of James II, upon the throne of Great Britain. He was a friend of political and religious liberty, a supporter of the new royal house, and his latest biographer, Professor Brodetsky, of the University of Leeds, says that he did much to make and keep Cambridge loyal to William and Mary. Moreover, Newton was already a man of distinction. The *Principia* had appeared ten years before, and the great achievements upon which his fame has rested ever since were known throughout the civilized world. Macaulay in telling of his second election to Parliament a few years later, says that Newton was the glory of the Whig party. This would indicate that as an official of the Whig administration his name might have had a political value.

In order, however, to give a truthful account of this great change in his life from the University to the Mint it is necessary to frankly say that Newton was an applicant for a place in the Government. At this time of his life he seems to have been in ill health, according to Brodetsky as the result of close application to his studies and irregular habits of eating and sleeping. He was a bachelor all his life and in the years of middle life had a tendency to be moody and unhappy. Although his scientific discoveries had brought him fame they had not brought him income and he seems to have felt depressed by his lack of means and what seemed to be an uninviting outlook for the future. Brodetsky thinks that his service in the House of Commons had something to do with making him discontented. At any rate he was in the hands of his friends for political preferment, apparently before the place in the Mint was considered for him. Great men have not been free from some of the minor weaknesses of mankind.

In 1694 his opportunity came through a friend high in the government. Charles Montague, later Lord Halifax, one of the most distinguished men of the time, had been a pupil of Newton's at Cambridge and a fellow-member of the Convention Parliament. Brewster, Newton's principal biographer, says that Montague "cherished for him the veneration of a disciple," and Montague became Chancellor of the Exchequer in 1694.

The coinage of the country at the time was in a terrible state of confusion and degradation. Until a period then recent the coins had been cut and stamped by hand. They were slightly irregular in shape and without the milled edge, hence both clipping and counterfeiting were comparatively easy, and although both practices were laid under the penalties for high treason they flourished prodigiously. The greater part of the old coins in circulation were either light-weights or counterfeits.

Macaulay's history gives a graphic account of daily quarrels in the market place over the coins, and of futile efforts by the government authorities tostop the tampering with them. Convictions and executions were daily occurrences, with sometimes half a dozen hangings at a time, but apparently without effect, except to develop popular sympathy for the offenders. Eventually the Government encountered the practical difficulties which usually attend upon efforts to enforce unpopular laws. Macaulay says that constables became unwilling to make arrests, justices unwilling to commit, witnesses unwilling to testify and juries unwilling to convict. Under these conditions some other course of action became imperative.

The coinage press, operated by horse-power, was devised and started up. It turned out pieces practically uniform in execution, which made counterfeiting far more difficult, and provided the milled edge, which readily exposed the work of the clipper. It was soon discovered, however, that the new coins when paid into circulation speedily disappeared. At first it seemed inexplicable that the public should decline to use new, fullweight, coins, instead of the worn and degraded pieces, but the reason soon became apparent. Why, indeed, should anybody pay out a new coin, containing a superior amount of silver, at the same value allowed for an old coin containing an inferior amount of silver? The new coins had a higher bullion value than the old, and that value could be realized abroad if not at home. A law prohibited the exportation of silver coin, but it was ineffective, for the coins could be melted down or evasion otherwise practiced. The new coins could not be made to circulate with the old.

W. A. Shaw, the English writer upon currency, commenting upon money-changing as it flourished in this period says:

"Given in one country an imperfect currency system, in which two elements of unequal value are concurrently circulating, and given no specific law of tender, and given no law for the withdrawal of worn or clipt specie, and given, with all this, another similarly imperfect currency system, in one or more countries near at hand, then the merchant exchanger, whether Italian or Jew, had close to his hand all the elements of an easy bargain.

He could buy up the good money by means of the bad, or the unworn money by means of the worn, or the more valuable money of one metal by means of the less valuable money of the other metal. He could in a retail way sell piece by piece the coin of one country to another country."

Montague, as Chancellor of the Exchequer, found the conditions of the currency intolerable and faced the necessity of doing something about it. It was an intricate problem, with various phases, one important question being whether the government should assume the loss which would result from melting down the old pieces, or require the holders to stand it. Moreover, as the work of the Mint would be greatly increased, an intelligent, honest, and efficient administration of that institution was of much importance. Montague consulted with Newton, John Locke and others upon the whole problem, and in March, 1696, addressed a letter to Newton, inviting him to accept the position of Warden of the Mint. This was not the highest position in the Mint, but the most responsible place in the operating force. The head of the institution was the Master of the Mint, to which place Newton was appointed in 1699, and held for the remainder of his life.

It is probable that Newton would not have wanted an office in which routine duties would take all of his time, to the exclusion of the studious pursuits in which he had been so much absorbed and in which he had become the world's greatest authority. He could not have been expected to abandon his interest in the problems which were commanding the attention of the scientific world, and nobody, certainly not such an admirer as Montague, would have wanted him to do that. In the letter tendering the place Montague says:

"Sir,—I am very glad that at last I can give you a good proof of my friendship, and the esteem the king has of your merits. Mr. Overton, the Warden of the Mint, is made one of the Commissioners of the Customs, and the king has promised me to make Mr. Newton Warden of the Mint. The office is the most proper for you. 'Tis the chief officer in the Mint. 'Tis worth five or six hundred pounds per annum, and has not too much business to require more attendance than you may spare. I desire you will come up as soon as you can, and I will take care of your warrant in the meantime. Pray give my humble services to John Lawton. I am sorry I have not been able to assist him hitherto, but I hope he will be provided for ere long, and tell him that the session is near ending, and I expect to have his company when I am able to enjoy it. Let me see you as soon as you come to town, that I may carry you to kiss the king's hand. I believe you may have a lodging near me.—I am, Sir, your most obedient servant,

"Chas. Montague."

Newton accepted and entered upon his duties at once. Whatever thoughts he may have had about continuing his former studies were banished for the time being, in view of the stupendous task of coinage then at hand. Macaulay says that "the ability, the industry and the strict uprightness of the great philosopher speedily produced a complete revolution throughout the department which was under his charge." The output of silver coin which previously had been about fifteen thousand pounds' worth per week, was speedily raised to one hundred and twenty thousands pounds' worth per week. This accomplishment was due in part to the opening of branch mints in other cities to facilitate the reception of old coins and distribution of the new, as well as for the increase of capacity. There is good reason for believing that Newton played an effective part in the enterprise, but it was an extraordinary undertaking and very likely the ability and interest of Montague, who had carried the adoption of the project over great opposition, had something to do with its efficient execution. The Chancellor, however, is quoted as saying that

[284]

without Newton he never could have carried it through.

Under the plan finally adopted, a future date was fixed at which the old coins should pass only in payments to the Government and a later date at which they should not pass at all. The clipped coins were redeemed at their full value. The country was engaged in a costly war on the continent at the time, and the Government's resources were taxed to the limit. In order to meet the loss in recoinage it was at first proposed to revive the old hearth money tax, but it was odious to the people, and Montague finally hit upon the window tax as less objectionable. The number of hearths in a home could not be certainly ascertained without entering, and every Englishman was taught that his home was his castle; therefore, it was thought better to tax the windows, which could be counted from outside. This was the origin of the window tax.

The recoinage task lasted about three years, and unquestionably was a great reform, creditable to all who had any part in it, but it did not dispose of all the problems related to the coinage. The old silver pieces were recoined at the weight and fineness that had been fixed in the reign of Queen Elizabeth. The new coins no longer had to meet the unfair competition of light-weight coins circulating at the same nominal value, but it was still apparent that the new money was being shipped out of the country. A factor in the situation more fundamental than clipping was responsible. A greater monetary problem was looming up, to-wit; that of maintaining the concurrent use of both gold and silver as money—a problem which was to vex the world for the next 200 years.

The gold coinage of Great Britain dates from the year 1663, when the Parliament passed an act providing for the guinea piece—so called because the first issue was coined from gold brought from the coast of Guinea—and gave it a legal tender value of twenty silver shillings. Down to that time silver had been the money of Great Britain, excepting copper and foreign gold coins. The latter were in use to a considerable extent, on account of their convenience for large payments, passing at their commodity value in shillings, either by agreement, custom, or the official ratings at which they were received at the Government offices. Silver was the standard of value, and this was true generally over Europe, The mines of the new world had flooded Europe with silver and the output of gold was comparatively small. Gold was too scarce and valuable to be the common medium of exchange. Hence it was that gold was generally valued in terms of familiar silver coins.

When the guinea was valued at twenty shillings that rating probably was close to the actual market value of that quantity of gold reckoned in full weight silver coins, but it was worth more in comparison with the abraded silver, and by 1696, when the recoinage began, under the continued deterioration of the silver coins the guinea was passing current at 28 to 30 shillings.

This currency of guineas above their legal tender value was by common consent. A debtor was not obliged to pay in guineas, for he had the right to pay in silver, but a creditor lost nothing by receiving gold at a premium, and the mutual convenience was served. Guineas were current at a rate in comparison with silver which made it profitable to import gold and export silver. Thus the circulation of silver diminished and the circulation of gold increased. The Government itself received and disbursed the gold coins at the Treasury offices at more than their nominal value, and from time to time published the rate at which it would receive them.

When the new silver coins were issued and the old ones had become illegal, of course the rating of the guinea was due to fall. The government at first fixed the new rate at twenty-two shillings, apparently recognizing that the legal rate of twenty shillings was too low even in comparison with full-

highest in Proportion to Silver, as in Spain and England.

"It is the Demand for Exportation which has raised the Price of exportable Silver about 2d. or 3d. in the Ounce Above that of Silver in Coin, and hath thereby created a Temptation to export or melt down the Silver Coin, rather than give 2d. or 3d. more for Foreign Silver; and the Demand for Exportation arises from the higher price of Silver in other Places than in England, in Proportion to Gold—that is, from the higher Price of Gold in England than in other Places, in Proportion to Silver, and therefore may be diminished by lowering the value of Gold in Proportion to Silver.

"If Gold in England, or Silver in East Indies, could be brought down so low as to bear the same Proportion to one another in both Places, there would be here no greater Demand for Silver than for Gold to be exported to India; and if Gold were lowered only so as to have the same Proportion to the Silver Money in England which it hath to Silver in the rest of Europe, there would be no Temptation to export Silver rather than Gold to any other part of Europe. And to compass this last there seems nothing more requisite than to take off about 10d. or 12d. from the Guinea, so that Gold may bear the same Proportion to the Silver Money in England which it ought to do by the Course of

Trade and Exchange in Europe. But, if only 6d. were taken off at present, it would diminish the Temptation to export or melt down the Silver Coin, and, by the effects, would show hereafter better than can appear at present, what further Reduction would be most convenient for the Publick.''

. . . .

''If Things be let alone till Silver Money be a little scarcer, the Gold will fall of itself, for People are already backward to give Silver for Gold, and will in a little time refuse to make Payment in Silver without a Premium, as they do in Spain; and this Premium will be an Abatement in the Value of Gold. And so the Question is, Whether Gold shall be lowered by the Government, or let alone till it falls of itself by the Want of Silver Money? It may be said, that there are great Quantities of Silver in Plate, and if the Plate were coined there would be no want of Silver Money. But I reckon that Silver is safer from Exportation in the Form of Plate than in the Form of Money, because of the greater Value of the Silver and Fashion together; and therefore I am not for coining the Plate till the Temptation to export the Silver Money, (which is a Profit of 2d. or 3d. an Ounce) be diminished: For as often as Men are necessitated to send away Money for answering

Debts Abroad, there will be a Temptation to send away Silver rather than Gold, because of the Profit, which is almost 4 per cent. And for the same Reason Foreigners will choose to send hither their Gold rather than their silver.''

What Newton says here is almost wholly incontrovertible. The only opinions he expresses are (1) that reason agrees with experience that silver flows from where it is of low value in proportion to gold to the countries where it is most highly valued, and (2) that if the existing situation was let alone silver probably would soon decline naturally as the result of changing conditions. In this second opinion he proved to be in error, for although the government decided to act upon his other suggestion by reducing the guinea rate from 21s. 6d. to 21s., this lowering of the value of gold was not sufficient to have the desired result. The act made both silver and gold legal tender at the ratio named, but silver was still under-valued and continued to be exported, while gold became in practice the sole legal tender and standard of value.

Although Newton had suggested the reduction of the rate to 21s. as possibly preliminary to a further reduction, no further reduction was made. The change in the value of the guinea to 21s. was the last attempt to secure the concurrent circulation of gold and silver in Great Britain, except as silver was later used for token money. In 1774 an act was passed limiting the legal tender powers of silver to £25, and in 1816 the single gold standard was definitely adopted and silver reduced to a token currency to prevent exportation.

Throughout the battle of the standards, which continued down to about 1900, the bimetalists endeavored to enlist the great authority of Newton's name on their side, basing their claims on the letter from which the foregoing extracts are taken. They argued that he had shown a preference for silver, although favoring the use of gold concurrently, with gold rated in silver. They argued also that it was comparatively unimportant that the parity of the two metals should always be exactly maintained, holding rather that the essential thing was to have one standard as the alternative of the other, as variations occurred in the production of the metals. They pointed to Newton's apparent indifference to any action in 1717, on the ground that the situation probably would cure itself, as evidence that he was the father of the alternative theory. In the later years of the controversy a very reputable body of support was developed in behalf of the project for an international agreement under which all nations would act together in fixing a coinage ratio for the two metals, thus putting an end to differing coinage ratios and the international shipments arising therefrom.

On the other hand, the adherents of the gold standard maintained that the relations between the metals which Newton described had conclusively shown that the values of the metals were fixed in the market place, not by legislation, and that he had proposed nothing but a temporary adjustment of relative values in accordance with previous practice. They held that the fluctuations in the production of the two metals made it useless to attempt to keep them in concurrent circulation, unless one was made the standard and the other subsidiary to it; also that while in the time of Newton it probably was sound policy to use the cheaper metal as the standard of value the vast trade and superior banking service of the later years of the nineteenth century made gold the metal best adapted to that purpose.

The truth is that Newton did not offer any theoretical discussion such as characterized the great controversy of the nineteenth century. Nobody was thinking of bimetalism by international agreement in his time and certainly it was not a practical proposition then whatever it may have been one hundred fifty or two hundred years later. He said nothing about monometalism, bimetalism or alternative standards. His letter is that of a responsible official, dealing with an immediate situation, and shows a complete comprehension of all the factors entering into it. Apparently the only purpose he had in mind at the time was to minimize the profit that was being made in the international traffic in coins. He told the Honorable Commissioners that silver was being taken out of Great Britain because it was undervalued there in comparison with its relation to gold in other countries, and that the movement could be stopped by raising the value of silver, or stating it the other way round by lowering the value of gold. He intimated, however, that a change of the legal rate was hardly worthwhile because the market rate probable would change again before long.

Great Britain actually was drifting to the gold standard. The volume of gold in circulation was increasing and the volume of silver was diminishing. John Locke was pronounced in his opinion that silver should remain the standard of value. If Newton thought so he did not say so, and the way to have secured that system was by slightly over-valuing silver instead of gold. On the other hand, if Newton thought that the tendency to acquire gold was in harmony with the increasing wealth of Great Britain, he did not offer any such plan for assuring the permanency of the gold standard as did Lord Liverpool one hundred years later.

Possibly he thought the time had not arrived for such legislation, which probably was true. Anyway, he did not enter into a comprehensive discussion of the subject. Macaulay says that he left no statement of his opinion upon the currency.

Aside from Newton's service in the recoinage and the fact that he did not choose to discuss the problem of the relations between the two metals except in a tentative manner, there is nothing of notable importance in his service at the Mint. After the great task of recoinage was out of the way he had time to indulge his natural taste for abstruse problems, but his great work in the field of natural science was done. Brodetsky says that he was not exhausted scientifically, but had made such stupendous scientific discoveries that he could not hope to improve upon them. The same writer sums up his career by saying that from 1665 to 1696 Newton was essentially a scientific researcher, laboring to unravel the laws of nature, while for an equal period, 1696 to 1727, he was the servant of the Nation and the foremost representative of British learning.

It would seem that the most natural explanation of the fact that his career after removal to London did not rival in achievements his career in the University is to be found in the varied demands and diversions of the later period. There is no reason to think that he had lost his interest in research or thought that the problems yet to be solved were of minor importance. Such an assumption is forbidden by an utterance which is completely in harmony with all that we know of him and has been universally regarded as a true expression of his character:

"I do not know what I may appear to the world; but to myself I seem to have been only like a boy playing on the seashore, and diverting myself in now and then finding a smoother pebble or a prettier shell than ordinary, whilst the great ocean of truth lay all undiscovered before me."

In his later years he leaned heavily upon John Conduitt, a highly valued assistant in the Mint, who married Newton's niece and succeeded him as Master of the Mint. There is abundant testimony that Newton always took his official responsibilities seriously and was an industrious and faithful public officer. His life in these closing years was spent in comfort and crowned with honors. He had income sufficient to enable him to live in good style and give aid to those in need who had claims upon him. His niece, who presided over his home, was a brilliant woman, well able to assist in the entertainment of congenial friends. His early service to the royal house had cemented a lasting friendship; he was knighted by Queen Anne in

1705. His health was good and all his faculties
well sustained to the last. He was President of the
Royal Society for the last twenty-four years of his
life, and the supreme figure in the world of Science.
He died in his eighty-fifth year.

John Winthrop

Engraved for The Colonial Society of Massachusetts from a portrait by
Copley, in possession of Harvard University.

NEWTON'S FIRST CRITICAL DISCIPLE IN THE AMERICAN COLONIES— JOHN WINTHROP

NEWTON'S FIRST CRITICAL DISCIPLE IN THE AMERICAN COLONIES—JOHN WINTHROP

FREDERICK E. BRASCH, M.S.

Library of Congress, Washington, D. C.

THE intellectual life of the colonial period of American history, namely, from 1636 to 1783, represents in part the western movement of the Renaissance of Europe. But from the standpoint of the history of science, the development of this movement in the colonies is yet very largely unknown history.

A study of the facts reveals that the intellectual progress of the mother countries of the various colonist groups is reflected in the achievements of the people of the new land. The several cargoes of human souls which the good ships of Captain John Smith, the *Mayflower*, and others, carried over half-charted seas and to unknown lands during the period from 1609 to 1650, brought with them the learning of the Universities of Oxford and Cambridge. In these ships came the Winthrops and John Harvard with the spirit and traditions of these schools.

Any orderly narration must not fail to give an

idea of the change of thought from the seventeenth
and eighteenth to the nineteenth century. The
educated Puritan is the typical man of the colonial
era and in his sombre dress and in his stilted manners
and speech we see the stamp of his religion and his
century. The mere struggle for existence consumed
most of his energies on week days and the God he
worshipped on Sundays was a stern and jealous one.
Hitherto science had given very little intelligent
explanation of the gigantic forces of nature, and
superstition was the natural outcome of the gross
ignorance of the times. The earth was only a
dismal cemetery. Ocean, mountains, forests, rivers
and lakes, the flush of spring and the colors of
autumn awoke no poetry in the Puritan soul.
Comets, shooting stars, thunderstorms and earthquakes and the Northern lights were messages from
the unseen world and usually regarded as omens of
disaster. The emotion they awakened was fear
rather than wonder and curiosity. It was natural
that the Mediaeval conception of astronomy should
attract the popular imagination and that the
Ptolmaic theory of the solar system should rest
lightly upon the Puritan mind.

Some books other than theological did find their
way to the centers of intellectual life of the colonies, but during this first hundred years they occupied space upon library shelves rather than in the

minds of those who would have profited most by them. However, in England the advent of the progressive spirit was being manifested in the revival of the philosophy of Roger Bacon through the thoughts of Francis Bacon and the Positive Empiricalism of John Locke. This was known as the age of criticism and the acquiring of knowledge by experimentation. How greatly this affected the colonial Puritanic theology and finally unshackled the minds of the learned Calvinists to a brighter world with sunshine and pure air will be noted as the subject of the paper is developed.

Not alone was the philosophy of man's moral and spiritual thoughts being worked out but also the science of man's relation to the physical world was being evolved and his conception of the universe was changing through the decline of Scholasticism. The attention of the mediaeval astronomer was focused on the true order of the planetary system of Copernicus, supported by the work of Kepler and Galileo, and later by Newton. However, progress in these matters was slow. The ideas of Gilbert on electricity and magnetism were not absolutely accepted; Boyle was developing chemistry from alchemy and mathematics was the only safe field for pure speculation. The Royal Society and other learned continental societies were fostered by the very daring of the seventeenth

[303]

century thinker. Oxford and Cambridge Universities now became the higher sources of our colonial intellectual life.

In the first quarter of the eighteenth century the effect of the progressive spirit of the rational knowledge of the mother country was felt by the alert and more progressive minds of the second generation in the colonies. Puritanic Calvinism found a double foe facing it squarely and firmly, on the shores of Massachusetts Bay Colony as well as in Connecticut, in the form of this new rationalism and met it with firm opposition. John Locke with positive empiricalism for Philosophy, and Sir Isaac Newton with mechanistic conception of the universe for Science, came with full force. In spite of the rule forbidding any delving into this new form of knowledge, secret progress was made.

Before we continue the history of this movement, let us for a brief moment see what actually constituted the center of learning established by the Puritan Fathers in 1636. In order to preserve the Christian spirit and the best of the learning from the mother country, the colonists founded a seminary for the education of their ministry. New Cambridge became a counterpart of Old Cambridge, for most of her tutors, as well as her greatest benefactor—a young non-conforming, dissenting minister, John Harvard, a graduate of Emanual College,

Cambridge—were educated in the eastern colleges. Theology and classics formed a large part of the spiritual and scholastic life of the new college, and Copernicus, Galileo and others were considered as innovators of whom no good was to be expected. Upon the death of John Harvard it was found that he had bequeathed his money and library—and incidentally his name—to the young college. However, the content of his library was not such as to excite or revolutionize the scholastic life. Nevertheless, the works of Thomas Aquinas, Bacon, Plutarch, Pliny and the classical authors fostered a new spirit and led to an interest in books of a larger scope.

The second of the great benefactors of Harvard was the Thomas Hollis family of bankers of London. We find among their many gifts of books a very good selection of the modern works of science of T. Brahe, Nich. de Cusa, Gassendi in *Astronomy*, Wallis's *Algebra*, Barrows' *Optics*, Galileo's *Dialogues*, Newton's *Optics*, Boyle's *Experiments*, and the transactions of the Royal Society. In fact, this list is known to have been comprised of the works of over a hundred and fifty of the best scholars of this period.

With the close of the seventeenth century, the library of Harvard College seems not to have possessed a copy of the works of Copernicus nor the first edition of Newton's *Principia*. The books used as the source of scientific instruction and astronomical knowledge were Gassendi's *Astronomy* based upon Copernicus and Galileo only, and Euclid's *Geometry*. Later Gravesand's *Natural Philosophy* came into use and displaced Gassendi. The former was the first introduction to Newton's philosophy in the colonies. Therefore, with the beginning of the eighteenth century, we find the works of Copernicus and Newton being studied from secondary sources, and yet progress was evidently made, for the minds of the Puritan scholars were showing the influence of new scientific ideas. Those who contributed most in the early period, by introducing Newton's philosophy, were Thomas Robie, Nathan Prince, and Isaac Greenwood.

Thomas Robie was the thirteenth of a long line of tutors who taught mathematics and natural philosophy at Harvard College. Robie was born in Boston in 1689 and graduated from Harvard in 1708, and six years later became a tutor in the college. He published an account of a remarkable eclipse of the sun, also a number of other scientific papers which were included in the transactions of the Royal Society. However, he is best remembered for the number of astronomical diaries he calculated and published from 1709–1720. This

[306]

was at that time considered evidence of scholarship and scientific attainment. The diary of 1709 was no doubt compiled to meet the requirements for the master of arts degree. Many of these diaries are no longer extant, but those that have been examined show the state of knowledge of astronomy at that period. The diary of 1720 contains an essay on the progress of the Copernican system as taking the place of the Ptolmaic doctrine and incidentally shows what Robie knew of Newton's work. President Leverett upon the death of Robie in 1729 makes the following statement to the overseers of the college, "It ought to be remembered that Mr. Robie was no small honor to Harvard College by his mathematical performance."

Nathan Prince, who succeeded Robie as tutor, was born near Boston in 1698 and graduated from Harvard in 1718, and five years later became tutor, which office he held until 1742. No astronomical diaries were computed by Prince nor were other scientific papers issued by him. He had, however, a reputation for superior genius in mathematics and natural philosophy and was said to have had no equal in New England—but nothing remains to sustain this high estimation. Prince died in Honduras in 1748.

Isaac Greenwood, born in 1702 and graduated from Harvard in 1721, became the first professor of mathematics and natural philosophy, a chair founded by the Hollis family through his influence. Greenwood comes nearer to possessing the high distinction of Newtonian scholar than either Robie or Prince, but his conduct in college made it necessary to retire him, after a service of ten years, in 1738. Nothing remains to justify claim to an honored career as a mathematics scholar. And the only records of his contributions to astronomy by way of Newtonian philosophy are his lectures in college, and a series of public demonstrations of which there is still extant a printed syllabus and advertisement. No comments are recorded as to what success he had as a teacher. Greenwood died in South Carolina in 1748. Robie, Prince and Greenwood introduced Newtonian ideas (only ideas) through secondary mediums—for as yet no copy of the *Principia* had reached their hands.

In the Virginia colonies, near Jamestown, was established the second college in America, founded in 1688. The College of William and Mary has recorded the establishment of the first professorship in mathematics with the first occupant of the chair the Rev. Hugh Jones of Oxford University. He came with scholarly attainment but no record exists as to his mathematical contributions, nor his knowledge of Newtonian philosophy.

In 1645 the Royal Society of London was founded

and immediately became the dominating force of scientific thought in England and on the continent, and in the American colonies as well. The relation of this society to the colonial life was very intimate and real. On the southern shores of the New England colonies was established a new form of government with its first governor the son of the first governor of Massachusetts. John Winthrop, Jr., was born in 1587. Shortly after his education was completed in Dublin, he followed his father to the New World. His interest in science was such that he became one of the earliest Fellows of the Royal Society, elected two years after its organization. Winthrop had a large correspondence with scientific men of his time—Boyle, Newton, Hooke, Napier and others. In fact, he became the western correspondent for the Society. His busy life as a colonial governor was not too absorbing to allow him to follow in the footsteps of Bacon in experimental science—but his investigations took the wrong direction, namely, Alchemy. His mind was of a practical turn and yet his interest in pure science enabled him to develop a spirit for research. In astronomy his knowledge was more advanced than that of the average colonist for he possessed a small telescope and made observations of a unique value. It is recorded as far back as 1664 that he made the astounding discovery of the ifth satelite of Jupiter, over two hundred years before it was actually discovered at Lick Observatory.

The second to honor the name of Winthrop in science for the colonies was John Winthrop, F.R.S., the grandson of the first governor of Connecticut. Born in 1681 and graduated from Harvard College in 1700, his chief claim to fame in history was as a a collector of over six hundred specimens of the flora as well as of the mineral kingdom of New England, under the auspices of the Royal Society. He became one of the most conspicuous members of the society and in honor of his service, the fortieth volume of the *Transactions* was dedicated to him. Winthrop died in England.

In 1701 the colonies were enriched by the founding of the third college. Yale College was first established at Saybrooke and later moved to New Haven. The first twenty years of its scholastic life rode upon financial and theological difficulties. Of its courses of study not much can be obtained, but it might be supposed that they were theological and classical and that the elements of Euclid were taught. About 1714 the college agent, then in London, succeeded in securing a collection of over seven hundred volumes for the impoverished college library and with these books came evidence of the new spirit of learning in England represented by

Locke, Boyle, Bacon, Milton and others. Through them came also the closest contact with the immortal Newton. Sir Isaac received the college agent, and handed him from his shelves the second edition of his *Principia*, just published, which contained the first announcement of the law of gravitation. He also gave a copy of his *Optics*. Halley gave his own edition of *Appollonius*. These books, however, did not remain long upon silent shelves. In the same year, an alert young Puritan named Samuel Johnson graduated from Yale. Johnson was immediately appointed tutor, and with a great desire to strengthen his learning as a theological student, he delved into this "feast set for kings." Newton's *Principia Mathamatica* absorbed him entirely to the exclusion of other subjects. He was aware of the new spirit that Locke and Bacon had aroused, and in Newton's work he found greater discipline for the inquiring mind. He offered instruction in Newton's philosophy in addition to tutoring in Alsted's *Geometry* and Gassendi's *Astronomy*. Even though he contributed no papers bearing evidence of his Newtonian studies, this scholar did much to vitalize metaphysical thought.

From this time on the history of philosophical thought in America showed an entirely different trend, due directly to the influence of Newton's ideas. Theology became the battleground for

[311]

moral and ethical theories developed from the idealism and empircal speculation brought to these shores by Locke and Newton.

A classmate and colleague of Johnson's, Daniel Browne, also became imbued with Newton's philosophy but he also left no records to support his claims to Newtonian discipleship. However, these two Yale scholars, due to their enthusiastic spirit for the new learning, were able to overthrow the Ptolmaic theory of the solar system, in which belief was at that time still as strong as it was in the Holy Scriptures, and to replace it with the modern astronomy of Copernicus. The period of this revival of empirical philosophy was of short duration. In five years both Johnson and Browne retired to continue their theological studies at Oxford and Cambridge. Johnson returned and became the first president of King's College (Columbia University). Browne died in England.

For the next twenty years Newton's *Principia* lay dormant at Yale and not until Thomas Clap, a graduate of Harvard College in 1722, became president of Yale in 1740, and again encouraged the study of higher mathematics, was it revived. With one exception, Clap had no equal in the colony as a scholar. His only scientific publication is a well thought out study on the motion of meteors based upon Newton's laws.

We have now brought our story of the early development of scientific thought in America down to the middle of the eighteenth century. We have outlined how the faint attempts to establish higher mathematical learning and a new philosophy based on the Newtonian doctrine, laid the foundation for what follows. The real Newtonian scholar is now to appear upon the scene. To meet him we must turn our thoughts back to Harvard at the time Yale received her first great gift. In 1714, the very year that Newton's *Principia* arrived in America, a child was born who was destined to carry the torch of Sir Isaac Newton to still greater heights and to maintain it there.

John Winthrop IV was a direct descendant of the Winthrops already referred to. We shall sketch his early life but briefly. We shall then analyse his contributions to the early astronomy and seek to justify the stand we have taken with regard to his place in the history of science in America—as its first astronomer and Newtonian disciple. Born in Boston, December 19, 1714, of parents already distinguished in the social and intellectual life of the community, he made rapid advancement in his studies. At the age of fourteen years, he graduated from the famous Boston Latin School. He then entered Harvard College and there established his place as one of the first students of his class. His great fondness for mathematical studies and experimental science, combined with a temperament tending toward idealism, soon led him to contemplation of the stars and the laws governing their motions. After his graduation from college in 1732 with the degree of Master of Arts, he retired to his father's home and for the next six years very little was known of him. However, from two precious manuscript commonplace books now preserved at Harvard College we find evidences of private study which forecast his future work. These books reveal his wide general reading, and recorded observations of natural phenomena such as sun-spots, magnetic variations and meteors, mathematical problems and philosophical meditations. Upon the forced retirement of his own professor, Isaac Greenwood, there was a vacancy in the Hollis professorship. The overseers of the college had not far to look for a successor. John Winthrop was appointed, at the age of twenty-four years, to become full professor of mathematics and natural philosophy, with two tutors as his assistants. Winthrop had been examined as to his proficiency in mathematics and the physical sciences, but the question of examining his religious statutes gave the authorities real concern. His views were suspected as being a little too broad for Harvard, even though his

[314]

ideas embodying the spirit of the Lockean or English philosophy of empiricalism were just the force that Harvard needed. At any rate, he was accepted on the first examination and passed over on the second, and duly inaugurated to the office which he held for the next forty years with honor and distinction to Harvard and to the history of cultural progress in America. Despite the predominance of orthodox clerical influence, this colonial scholar was not without liberty in the examination of truth according to the modern method. He found his way by setting aside any metaphysical controversy and sought freedom by the enlightened scientific methods of Bacon, Descarte and Newton. Having thus far secured his fundamental understanding of Newton's principles of celestial mechanics through secondary sources, he soon secured for himself the original. He acquired this the year after he was introduced to his professorship, 1739. At the age of twenty-five, we find Winthrop assiduously engaged in mastering the Principia which he so brilliantly applied to all his long years of subsequent work in astronomy and natural philosophy and in research and class instruction.

To Yale College belongs the honor of having received the first copy brought to the colony of Newton's *Principia*, second edition, 1713, and we must give John Winthrop credit for having secured the second copy in America—third edition, 1726. Winthrop's copy of the *Principia* belonged to the last edition published during Newton's life time. It contains all the additions made by the author in the 1713 edition and is the one upon which all subsequent ones are based. It was edited by Pemberton and contains a new preface by Newton. No copy of either the first edition or its second issue ever reached the shores of the western world during colonial days. Both of these issues of the immortal work were very limited in number and were immediately absorbed in England and on the Continent.

Winthrop began his work under very auspicious conditions in so far as scientific books were concerned. That he was liberal in his individual tastes is evidenced by a study of the catalogue of the books in his private library. His collection of scientific works was, as Thomas Jefferson said, one of the finest of the day. With a good working library, let us see what instrumental equipment he had access to before proceeding to the results of his energy. The modern laboratory was not known then, but Winthrop possessed apparatus which will illustrate the fundamental facts of natural philosophy then known. "For Astronomy," he says, "we had before been supplied by ·

Mr. Hollis with telescopes of different lengths, one of 24 feet; and a brass quadrant of two feet radius, carrying a telescope of greater length, which formerly belonged to the celebrated Dr. Halley. We had also the most useful instrument for dialing; and for surveying, a brass semi-circle, with plain sights, and magnetic needles. Also a curious telescope, with a complete apparatus for taking the difference of leveling. From a number of gentlemen of the province the following additions were received: a fine reflecting telescope of different magnifying powers, and adapted to different observations. Microscopes of the several sorts now in use; Hadley quadrant, fitted in a new manner, a nice variation compass, and dipping needles with instruments for the several magnetical and electrical experiments."

From an original manuscript notebook in the library of Harvard College we find the first authentic astronomical observations made by Winthrop, dated April 19, 20, 21, 22, 1739, on sunspots (with an 8-foot telescope). There are several well-executed drawings, showing the positions, apparent movement and structure of the spots. He also made observations as to their physical character but does not enter upon any discussion as to the theory of their origin. He did recognize them, however, as an integral part of the sun and not

[317]

something wholly unrelated or detached. These seem to be the first scientific observations on sun-spots in America.

The next undertaking to engage our astronomer's attention (we must remember that he was also fully occupied with the teaching duties of his office) was the study of the Transit of Mercury over the sun, April 27, 1740. Winthrop was fully aware of the importance of transit observations, especially those of Venus, and therefore proposed to observe these rare phenomena with well thought out methods. Having procured his *Principia* and mastered the principles of the laws of gravitation and celestial motion, he was anxious to test Newton's theories for his own satisfaction,and thereby advance science.

Winthrop had accepted as his authority Halley's tables and ephemerides of planetary motion, which were in use. He was advised that the former part of this transit would be visible in his horizon, and therefore resolved to observe it with an instrument he already possessed; namely, the 24-foot Huyghens' telescope.

The qualitative results are probably not greatly different from our present knowledge of such transits, but it is in the methods of arriving at these results that the vast improvements have been made. Without the modern clocks, chronographs and

electric circuit breaks—also firmly mounted telescopes with all the accessories—it is to be wondered
that Winthrop accomplished his task at all.   There
is something inspiring in the spirit and zeal with
which such pioneering work is sometimes accomplished.   And Winthrop, with his splendid scientific qualifications and thorough knowlege and
understanding of the theory of planetary motion,
accomplished his task with such a marked degree of
success, that his work was accepted by the Royal
Society of London and published in full in the
Transactions.   Winthrop was thanked by the Royal
Society and asked to continue his communications,
which immediately gave him high rank and finally
led to his election as a Fellow.

After the first flush of success and professional
recognition, he continued to lay before the Royal
Society of London further results of his astronomical research.   He followed his first paper with the
observations of the second Transit of Mercury on
October 25, 1743, and again a third Transit on
November 9, 1769.   The problems in these transits
which interested Winthrop were: the exact determination of longitude between Cambridge and
London, the equation of time, the position of
Mercury's nodes, its inclination and hourly motion.
Winthrop was more than interested in ascertain-
ing the correctness of Newton's laws of motion

[319]

from celestial phenomena for he also prepared and established the first laboratory of experimental physics in this country to test the laws of gravitation of bodies on the earth. In conjunction with these experiments, he demonstrated to his students the motions of planets and comets, and illustrated the problems of eclipses, etc. Far more significant than this, however, was the first practical demonstration and experiment in electricity and magnetism in a laboratory in America. Of course these lecture experiments had to do also with problems of the elements of mechanics, hydro-statics, optics, heat, and the theory of light and prisms according to Newton. These experimental lectures which were given by Winthrop himself before the class were conducted much as are those in a modern laboratory—except that today the students perform the work themselves. The original notes and lectures, in book form, are preserved in the Harvard library. Winthrop's lectures were held in the Hollisian philosophical apparatus chamber at Harvard College. The experiments were extended over a long period. They began in 1746 and continued up to 1771, and probably to 1779. It was this work of Winthrop's which laid the solid foundation of Harvard's preeminence in science, and inspired the spirit of research which has made this country outstanding in the history of science.

It was during 1771 that Count Rumford, as a student at Harvard, attended Winthrop's lectures and thus derived his first knowledge of heat and other properties of matter. He said, "I made sufficient progress in Natural Philosophy under this excellent and happy teacher."

It has recently come to light that the first introduction into our colleges of the elements of fluxions now known as calculus, was in connection with the thesis required of the students under Winthrop, beginning about 1751. This marks a definite epoch in mathematical studies which has interested students of history for some time.

The year 1755 was a memorable one to the inhabitants of New England, due to the occurrence of an earthquake of some severity. The study of this phenomenon called forth Winthrop's best endeavors and revealed at the same time a large and broadminded scientist. As a theorist, he probably was more modern than he has been given cerdit for. His observations, deductions, and the theory he advanced, besides the theological implications, were given in two lectures in the Holden Chapel before the students and faculty.

The whole treatise shows an exceptionally comprehensive study. It is also a curious intermixture of analytical chemistry, mineralogy, geology, and astronomy.

[321]

Winthrop is often called our first seismologist. He was the first in this country to apply true inductive methods to observations of the earth-movement, and to advance the theory that the disturbances of the earth-crust were in the form of waves, and transmitted a pendulum-like motion to buildings and objects on the surface. He was the first to apply computation to the phenomena, consequently discovering the analogy between seismic motion and musical vibrations; he also discovered the principle that the quicker the motion the shorter the wave length of the disturbance. His ideas on the nature of heat were new to the science of geology, especially those relating to the internal actions of volcanoes and earth-movements.

In view of the fact that his period lacked trained men to observe and study such phenomena, and also lacked the instruments and methods for recording their effects, it is surprising that his deductions were so complete and accurate.

Winthrop's theological views, liberally interspersed with his scientific observations, were not unduly incongruous with the general spirit of science or scientific belief. While he may have separated the idea that such phenomena of nature as earthquakes, were not the direct expression of the wrath of God, he did not completely abandon the dualistic doctrine held so tenaciously by the puritan inhabitants of old New England. This was one of the objects of his public lectures,— primarily to alleviate the fears, supersition, and ignorance concerning the significance of such phenomena, since the credulous puritans were not yet entirely ready for purely scientific explanations of natural phenomena.

Winthrop's next public work was two lectures upon comets, and in particular on the return of the comet (1682) better known as Halley's comet, which he was fortunate to observe, since it was the first predicted return of a comet. This lecture was also read in the Chapel of Harvard College, April 11, 1759, as a part of the regular and assigned duty of the Hollis professorship. Winthrop first observed this comet on April 3, after it had passed perihelion, and, like similar celestial phenomena, had caused much anxiety and speculation as to its meaning.

In the first lecture his introduction to the subject of comets is descriptive, showing the relation and differences between comets, fixed stars and planets. This is followed by a history of their discovery with various theories concerning their origin and nature, especially during the preceding two hundred years.

His own observations and theories are, however, well worth considering, in their relation to astronomic thought and its bearing upon history. Winthrop has revealed himself as a mathematical and theoretical astronomer, but he has also proved his ability as a capable and practical observer. He computed the orbital elements of one of the comets under observation during this period; and his work upon the geometrical demonstrations, suggested by Newton, concerning the ascent of the tails of comets received laudable notices from the Royal Society. This paper, the original of which was in Latin, entitled "Cogitata de Cometis," was communicated to the Society by Dr. Franklin on May 6, 1766, and read March 19, 1767. It contains five problems, with dependent scholia and corollaries. In these he investigates the limits of attraction between the comets and the sun, and the laws of motion and direction by which an elastic fluid or vapor arising from the head of a comet would be governed. He also deduces the masses and densities of comets from the observed breadth of the coma in the side next to the sun. In this method, which he considers as entirely new to science, he infers that the density of the comet of 1665 was to the density of the earth as 350 to 1; and that of the comet of 1682, as 5 to 11; and suggests an analogy in this respect, between comets and planets; that the densities are greater in proportion to their nearness to the sun.

[324]

His explanation of the curved appearance of the tails of comets, which are occasionally manifested, contains this remark—"that as no incurvature or deviation from the opposition to the sun is perceived, but what may arise from the progressive motion of the head around the sun, it appears probable that comets do not revolve on their axes."

In his second discourse before the college community April 18, 1759, he discussed the true theory of comets according to the work of Newton's *Principia*, and also according to the laws formulated by Kepler, with the predictions of Halley. As in all his previous papers or lectures, Winthrop shows a profoundness of learning and authority. This is further evident from the mathematical computations connected with the solution of the orbital elements, and the origin of periodic comets, according to Halley.

In 1769 Winthrop published an account in the Boston journals of the observations of the brilliant comet which appeared on September 1. The remarkable feature of this comet was the length of its tail, which his measurements showed to be 45 degrees.

Again in 1770, in June, a remarkable comet appeared and passed its perihelion point in August. This comet had no tail and was noted for its swiftness, for it described in one day an arc of more than

40 degrees. Winthrop ascribed this excessive
motion to the fact of its approach to the earth on
that day to within one-fiftieth part of the earth's
distance from the sun. He observed this comet
with care and the observations enabled him to
calculate its orbital elements.

A more complete analysis of this colonial astronomer's knowledge of comets is not possible here,
but further mention would be of interest and importance to the study of the history of astronomy in
America.

As will be noted, Winthrop had no stated
program by which to observe the "nightly heavens"
regularly, as the modern astronomers have. He
had no problems requiring long and continuous use
of instruments and calculation for final solution.
His was, essentially, the work of a pioneer laboring
when time from his daily task would permit. Thus,
again we find him in 1761 preparing, with foresight
and diligence, plans to observe two events of great
astronomical importance which took place in this
country—the transits of Venus, in 1761 and 1769.
Winthrop's keen sense of appreciation of the value
of such opportunities was of vital significance in
America's astronomical history. This is evident
from the introduction to his first discourse in 1769
on the use of the transit of Venus.

The first astronomical expedition in this country

was that in which Harvard College and the Province of Massachusetts participated. That Harvard
had a scholar so well trained, and disposed to
undertake this scientific mission, speaks well for
her eminence in science at that period. The
ultimate success of this work depended upon the
cooperation of many astronomers. European observatories, Greenwich and Paris, sent out five
different observing parties to America. In Philadelphia, the American Philosophical Society
authorized David Rittenhouse and a number of
prominent gentlemen to make all preparation to
observe this transit also.

A special act of the Massachusetts government
granted the use of the Province sloop to convey
Winthrop and two assistants, with instruments
loaned by the College, to St. John's, Newfoundland. So, provided with a reflector having two
wires, vertical and horizontal, and a clock, and all
adjustments made, Winthrop says, "we waited for
the critical hour, which proved favorable to our
wishes." On June 6 the sun rose at St. John's at
4^h 18^m with Venus upon its disk. He applied
himself faithfully in observing the passage of the
planet over the sun, one assistant counting at the
clock, the other recording the time and the observations made by Winthrop.

Without giving full details of the time of contacts and measurements of the passage of Venus across the sun, it is sufficient to say that the results of the calculations gave the parallax of the sun as 8".25. This value is apparently not the mean value of the parallax as it was derived from one set of observations based upon Halley's method; namely, the "method of duration," that is, observation of the contacts, and also of the position of the planet on the sun. While Winthrop observed this transit very thoroughly and made careful computations, yet his instruments and methods were naturally not such as to give results to be compared with those of Newcomb and others from the transits of 1878 and 1882. However, he later gathered all available observations, and from these determinations found the sun's parallax, at its mean distance from the Earth, to be 8" .68, which is comparable with the present accepted value. In the second transit of Venus (June 3, 1769), which again called forth important preparations both in Europe and the Colonies, similar observations were made by Winthrop in Cambridge, by West in Providence, and by Rittenhouse in Philadelphia.

The astronomer-royal, Dr. Maskelyne, had urged Winthrop to plan for observations in the Lake Superior region, where both the beginning and end were visible. But to his great disappointment, his health would not permit the long and rigorous journey. Consequently, Winthrop could only observe the first two contacts of this transit as the last two occurred at sunset (New England time). Again our colonial astronomer made a detailed study of all the observations available, both of this transit and of that of 1761; but the results exceeded the computed values of parallax given by him on his second lecture.

In order to obtain a clearer historical interpretation of this scholar's ideas and knowledge of the problems of astronomy, and those involved in transit observations, the following extracts of his first and second lectures upon the subject are given verbatim: "A transit of Venus over the sun is the most uncommon and most important phenomenon that the whole compass of astronomy affords us. So uncommon is it, that it can never happen above twice in any century; in others but once; and in some centuries it cannot happen at all. And the importance of it is such as to supply us with a certain and complete solution of a very curious problem, which is inaccessible in any other way. On both accounts it well deserves a very particular attention."

"So extremely rare are these phenomena, and in fact till that which was observed in 1761, there never had been but one seen since the creation."

It would seem that with all his varied interests—

his astronomical problems, his duty as a teacher, his special lectures before the public—Winthrop's time was fairly well occupied. He was nevertheless able to find leisure to follow very closely the work of Benjamin Franklin upon electricity. Franklin found in Winthrop his main support for the theories and conclusions relative to his experiments. The relation of earthquakes to lightning had become a theological question in the colonies and one which gave them much concern. The clergy believed that the "ironpoints" invented by Franklin and erected to protect the houses from lightning, were really means of conducting electricity to the ground and that the release of this electricity from the ground caused earthquakes. Winthrop was frequently called upon to defend Franklin from attacks on this score. One of the early theological-scientific debates was between Winthrop and Thomas Prince, a Boston divine. Its subject was the relation of electricity to earthquakes and the theology implicated in the question was also discussed. It is impossible, of course, to give the details of this debate here, but the fact remains that Winthrop established a clearer understanding of these two phenomena of nature and Franklin's "ironpoints" still exist.

In conjunction with his interest in electricity, our colonial scientist carried on magnetic and meteorological observations. Records of these observations and computations are still preserved. The results have been found so reliable and accurate that they have been incorporated in a volume of the Unites States Coast and Geodetic Survey. The series of observations runs from 1672 to 1800 and shows a range of declination of the magnetic needle with the magnetic pole from 11°.15–5°.22 at Boston.

From 1672 to 1742 Winthrop copied principally from Halley's observations; from 1742 to 1775 he observed in Boston; from 1775 to 1800 he computed the magnetic deflection. Surveying and navigation were at that time the most important professions and Winthrop intended his observations to be of great service in these two fields. His mind was a characteristically practical one and it was not his purpose to develop a theory of magnetism. However, in the more theoretical aspect of electricity, he does allow himself freedom for speculative interpretation, for we find him in correspondence with Franklin regarding an observation on atmospheric electricity. This seems to have been the first of its kind in the colonies and is therefore of such importance that I shall venture to read it as he words it:

"There is an observation relating to electricity in the atmosphere, which seemed new to me, though perhaps it will not to you: However, I will venture to mention it. I have some points on the top of my house, and the wire where it passes within-side the house is furnished with bells, according to your method, to give notice of the passage of the electric fluid. In summer, these bells generally ring at the approach of a thunder cloud; but cease soon after it begins to rain. In winter, they sometimes, though not very often, ring while it is snowing; but never, that I remember, when it rains. But what was unexpected to me was, that though the bells had not rung while it was snowing yet the next day, after it had done snowing, and the weather was cleared up; while the snow was driven about by a high wind at W. or N. W. the bells rung for several hours (though with little intermissions) as briskly as ever I knew them, and I drew considerable sparks from the wire. This phenomenon I never observed but twice; viz. on the 31st of January, 1760, and the 3d of March, 1762.''

Paralleling his observations on earthquakes and magnetic variations, Winthrop also records with some regularity the appearance of the Northern Lights from 1741 to 1757. His work upon meteorology was also of importance, but time does not permit an account of this. We must be content to say that the observations which he began have their place in the history of meteorology in this country and are still continued. He gathered observations from many sources as well as places and made the reductions necessary for the results he was interested in obtaining. In many respects Winthrop ante-dates our modern astronomer with his early statistical methods, for we find him gathering data running into long series on earthquakes, meteorology, magnetic observations, comets, transit observations, and making synthetical studies. Among a host of minor problems which he thought of sufficient importance to study, observe and record were: the physical appearance of Venus during transit over the sun, eclipse of Jupiter's satellites, lunar and partial solar eclipses, abberation of light, sunspots and the computing of orbital elements of comets. These observations were not sent to the Royal Society. In all, however, he sent ten major papers to the Society. There were also published in the Boston newspapers numerous accounts of such celestial phenomena as might interest the credulous public of his time.

Winthrop's lectures upon Earthquakes, Comets and Transit of Venus were contained in six published booklets and these will probably become classics in scientific literature and form the foundation for the history of scientific progress in America. There is also extant a series of twenty-five letters bearing particularly upon Halley's comets and the theory of Jupiter's influence according to Newton. The recipient of these letters was Rev. Ezra Stiles. A number of letters written to Franklin bear upon electricity and the theory of atmospheric electricity. Winthrop's lectures and letters not only reveal the scholar and scientist and offer convincing proof of his knowledge of Newtonian doctrines, but they also show his originality and power of analysis.

There is another outstanding fact concerned with the history of our country's intellectual progress that is not generally known—namely, that the founding of the American Academy of Arts and Sciences can be attributed directly to Winthrop. With a strongly intellectual community now developing in Boston, our Winthrop found great need of further expression of scientific ideas. He was a close friend of John Adams and both of them were more or less jealous of the advances that Philadelphia was making in various ways. On several occasions both gentlemen discussed the possibility of founding an Academy in Boston similar to the American Philosophical Society. Winthrop's health and manifold duties did not permit an active part in this undertaking but you will note that all of the best students who graduated under him are among the incorporators of

[334]

the American Academy. During the trying times of the Revolution with the mother country from 1775 to 1779, our scholar was an ardent patriot and espoused the cause of the colony. He was a a councillor and friend of Washington and of others who stood high in the founding of the New Republic.

From this brief survey of the life and work of our first American astronomer we are led to wonder how he was able to initiate in a pioneer sense and accomplished so much with distinction and faithfulness. We can account for this, I think, from the fact that Winthrop was by temperament an ideal student. He had, too, an ideal home which made it possible during his many spells of illness to carry on.

He was asked twice during his forty years of teaching to become president of Harvard College, but he lacked the physical endurance for this position. Winthrop was medium in build and active in spite of his not being very robust. In appearance he was thoughtful and dignified. We can picture him crossing the college yard clad in the colonial robe that was worn by scholars in those days, with his well-shaped head covered by a wig. On the walls of the faculty room at Harvard there is a portrait of Winthrop sitting at a table upon which stands a reflecting telescope and a large book, supposed to be his copy of Newton's *Principia*.

Winthrop was honored as no man of his time had been. He was easily recognized as the most learned and capable of men during a period of over forty years of service to Harvard College. The Royal Society elected him as a Fellow in 1765 and the American Philosophical Society enrolled him as a member in 1768. From the University of Edinburgh he received the honorary degree of LL.D and his Alma Mater conferred the same degree upon him in 1773—the first honorary degree of Doctor of Law conferred by Harvard University. Winthrop was married twice and one of his sons, James, attained some degree of eminence as a scholar in science.

In Cambridge on May 3, 1779, at the age of sixty-five, John Winthrop, scholar, scientist, and astronomer, passed away in the fulness of his fame. He lies buried with his ancestors in the old King's Chapel burying ground, Boston.

CONCLUSION

Beginning with Archimedes in the middle of the third century B.C., and coming down through the intervening centuries to Galileo and Kepler, the mechanistic conception of the universe was in process of evolution.

We have knowledge of the fundamental contributions Newton has made to mathematics,

astronomy and physics. We also have had proof
that no single book in the empirical sciences has
been of more importance in developing the present
conception of our philosophy of nature, than the
Principia Mathematica. The place of this book in
the history of science is also an honored one.

Newton's philosophy gave rationalistic order
to scientific thought and Winthrop, with his keen
and positive mathematical intuition, responded
quickly to Newton's doctrines. (Remember that
he was only twenty-five years old when he first
possessed a copy of the *Principia*.) He became
thoroughly converted to the new spirit of science
and never doubted the validity of the relation of
terrestrial mechanics to celestial space. His contemporaries, Ezra Stiles, Thomas Clap, Benjamin
Franklin and his colleagues at Harvard College
recognized in him our first mathematical scholar and
they considered him superior as a Newtonian
disciple to any to be found in the mother country.
Bradley and Halley may have been his equals.
Winthrop's reputation was even greater abroad
than it was at home.

Winthrop was quite capable of making independent discoveries, but he was essentially a
teacher and interpreter of the truths of nature as
manifested by the laws of Newton's philosophy.
He established no school of thought. His mission

was rather to advance science along rational lines through Newton's doctrines and to place modern science in America on the high plane of idealism it has since maintained.

Winthrop's last paper to the Royal Society, dated January 20, 1774, was as a final tribute to Newton when he challenged Castillion for a statement made in his *Life of Sir Isaac Newton*. This author misinterpreted Newton's methods of handling certain problems and credited Descartes with a superior method. Winthrop in his usual direct and scholarly manner defends the issue in favor of Newton and asks leave to submit the arguments to the judgment of the Royal Society.

I am sure that Newton himself could not have wished for a more brilliant and gifted scholar nor a more ardent and sincerely devoted disciple to represent him in the western movement of the Renaissance of science and civilization, than John Winthrop. Through him the torch of Newton has been handed down these one hundred and fifty years to Peirce and Newcomb and to our own distinguished group of today and now we glory in the light of the *Principia* which has played such a large part in giving to astronomy in America the preeminence it holds in contemporary science.

APPENDIX

APPENDIX

MEETING COMMEMORATING THE BICENTENARY OF NEWTON'S DEATH

HELD AT THE

AMERICAN MUSEUM OF NATURAL HISTORY
NEW YORK

November 25 and 26, 1927

---

*Under the Auspices of The History of Science Society in
Collaboration with The American Astronomical Society,
The American Mathematical Society, The American
Physical Society, The Mathematical Association
of America, and Various other
Organizations*

PROGRAM

First Session

Professor David Eugene Smith, President of the History of
Science Society, Presiding

Introductory Address on Newton's Life and Work. David
Eugene Smith, Columbia University.

Newton and Optics. Dayton C. Miller, Case School of
Applied Science.

Newton's Philosophy of Gravitation with Special Reference
to Modern Relativity Ideas. George D. Birkhoff,
Harvard University.

Newton's Influence on the Development of Astrophysics.
W. W. Campbell, University of California.

[341]

Second Session

Professor E. W. Brown, Presiding

Newton and Dynamics. M. I. Pupin, Columbia University.

Newton as an Experimenter. Paul R. Heyl, United States Bureau of Standards.

Developments Following from Newton's Work. E. W. Brown, Yale University.

Newton's Twenty Years Delay in Announcing the Law of Gravitation. Florian Cajori, University of California. (Read in part by Dr. Lao G. Simons.)

Newton's Early Study of the Apocalypse. Florian Cajori. (Read by title.)

Newton's Fluxions Florian. Cajori. (Read by title.)

Third Session

Professor Lyman C. Newell, Presiding

Newton's Work in Alchemy and Chemistry. Lyman C. Newell, Boston University.

Newton's Place in the History of Religious Thought. George S. Brett, Toronto University.

Newton in the Mint. George E. Roberts, The National City Bank of New York.

Newton's First Critical Disciple in the American Colonies,— John Winthrop. Frederick E. Brasch, Library of Congress.

EXHIBITION OF NEWTONIANA AND RELATED MATERIAL

In connection with the meetings held at the American Museum of Natural History there was an exhibition of material relating to Newton, his contemporaries, the predecessors to whom he stated his indebtedness, and those of his successors who developed further his scientific theories. The collection consisted of upwards of a hundred portraits of Newton, more than twenty-five portrait medals and tokens, numerous autographs and other specimens of his writing, and a large number of editions of his works. There were also many portraits, autograph letters, medals, and published works of scholars whose contributions to science were related to those of Newton.

I. From the Babson Institute Collection, Wellesley, Massachusetts

1. Collections for the History of the Town and Soke of Grantham containing authentic memoirs of Sir Isaac Newton. By Edmund Turner. 1806. It also contains the pedigree of Newton, copied verbatim from the entry made by Sir Isaac Newton, with his affidavit accompanying it.
2. Geographia Generalis. By Bernhardi Vareni. 1672. Newton assisted in editing this work.
3. Fluxions. Translated by Colson. 1736. It contains a note by a contemporary owner, dated 1737.
4. Note by an anonymous translator, referred to in No. 3.
5. Commercium Epistolicum. 1732. Relates to the priority controversy.
6. French Translation of Commercium Epistolicum.
7. Account of the Commericum Epistolicum. Published by order of the Royal Society, concerning the dispute between Leibniz and Keill about the right to the invention of the method of Fluxions by some called the differential method. Transactions of the Royal Society of London. 1714.
8. Principia. First edition, 1687.
9. Principia. A re-issue of the first edition, 1687. This has

a new title page, containing a different imprint from the first issue of the first edition.

10. Principia. Second edition, 1713.

11. Principia. Third edition, 1726.

12. Motte's Translation of Newton's Mathematical Principles of Natural Philosophy. Vol. I. First edition 1729. 2 vols.

13. Motte's Translation of Newton's Mathematical Principles of Natural Philosophy. Vol. II. First edition. 1729.

14. First American Edition of Motte's Translation of the Principia. 1850. Published for use in American Schools and dedicated to the Teachers of the Normal School of the State of New York.

15. A View of Sir Isaac Newton's Philosophy. By Henry Pemberton, 1726.

16. Gravesande's Mathematical Elements of Natural Philosophy Confirmed by Experiments. Translated by J. T. Desaguliers. Fifth edition, 2 vols., 1737.

17. Rohault's System of Natural Philosophy. Illustrated with Dr. Samuel Clarke's notes taken mostly from Sir Isaac Newton. 2 volumes. The original of this book was in Latin, published 1702. The translation is by John Clarke.

18. Commentaries on the Principia. By Nicholas Saunderson. Neatly written manuscript bound in panelled calf.

19. Sir Isaac Newton's Mathematical Philosophy. With Dr. Halley's Account of Comets. Illustrated. By William Whiston. 1716.

20. Newtonia System of Philosophy. Familiarly Explained 2nd ed. 1762. London.

21. The Chronology of Ancient Kingdoms. Amended, with a preface by John Conduitt. 1728.

22. Observations upon the prophecies of Daniel and the Apocalypse of St. John. 1733.

23. Newton for the Ladies! This book was written in 1739 by Algarotti especially that Italian women might know something about Newton's Theory of Light and Color. It is a presentation copy from the author and contains some original verses by him. The binding is old red morocco, tooled, with edges tooled and gilded.

24. Sir Isaac Newton's Philosophy explained for the Use of Ladies. A translation of Algarotti's work, by Elizabeth Carter. 1739.

25. This is Vol. V of Bishop Horsley's collected works of Newton. This is considered the best collection of his works and was published in five volumes from 1779 to 1785.

26. Opticks. First edition. 1704.

27. Opticks. Second edition. 1717. The original issue of the second edition. It is rare, most copies being of the second issue of 1718. This copy is of great interest for having belonged to Sir Isaac Newton himself, who made additions and corrections (all verified to be in his own handwriting). These were wholly or partly adopted in the later editions of the Opticks.

28. Opticks. Second edition with additions. 1718.

29. Opticks. Third edition.

30. Opticks. Fourth edition. 1730.

31. The Countermine. This book was in Sir Isaac Newton's library and has his autograph on the front leaf.

32. Experimentorum Novorum Physico-mechanicorum. By Robert Boyle. 1680. This book was in Sir Isaac Newton's private library and bears his autograph. It was evidently a gift from the author himself to Sir Isaac.

33. A book from Newton's Library. This very interesting collection of translations of letters on the Newton-Leibniz controversy on the invention of the calculus was evidently prepared for Newton when he issued the Second edition of the Commercium Epistolicum. There are also other manuscripts bound up with these letters. Note the corrections in Newton's handwriting.

34. A Demonstration of some of the Principal Sections of Sir Isaac Newton's Principles of Natural Philosophy. By John Clarke, D.D. 1730. This is one of the first English books printed after Newton's death treating of his great discoveries.

35. Correspondence of Sir Isaac Newton and Professor Cotes, including letters of other men. Edited by J. Edleston, M.A. 1850.

II. *From the Library of George A. Plimpton, LL.D.*

1. Philosophiae Naturalis Principia Mathematica. Cambridge, 1713.

2. Philosophiae Naturalis Principia Mathematica. Amsterdam, 1714.

3. Principia. Translated into English by Andrew Motte. To which are added the Laws of the Moon's Motion, according to Gravity. By John Machin. 2 vols., London, 1729.

4. Philosophiae Naturalis Principia Mathematica. Le Seur and Jacquier Edition. 3 vols., Geneva, 1739–1742.

5. Principia. Cambridge, 1765.

6. Principia. Perpetuis Commentariis Illustrata. Editio Nova. Summa Cura Recensita. Le Seur et Francisci Jacquier.

7. Opuscula Mathematica, Philosophica et Philologica. Parts I–III. Lausanne and Geneva, 1744.

8. Arithmetica Universalis; Sive de Compositione et Resolutione Arithmetica Liber. 1732.
9. Optica. Samuel Clarke edition. London, 1706.
10. Optica. M. Beauzee. Paris, 1787.
11. Vincent Wing. Harmonicon Coeleste. London, 1651. Newton's copy, with notes and numerous corrections and additions in his handwriting.
12. Newton's copy of Journal, with two signatures and numerous notes in Newton's handwriting.

III. From the Newton Collection of David Eugene Smith, LL.D.

1. First Edition of Lord Brougham's Address on Newton, with his autograph changes for the Second edition. London, 1858.
2. Lord Brougham's Tracts, London, 1860, including his address on Newton, with the changes made as shown in the above copy of the first edition. Presentation copy from the author.
3. Bishop Berkeley's attack on Newton's Philosophy. London, 1734. Presentation copy from the author to Sir Thomas Hammer, Speaker of the House of Commons.
4. Optical Lectures of Newton. English Translation. London, 1728.
5. Universal Arithmetic. Raphson's Translation from the Latin. London, 1720.
6. Arithmetica Universalis, with commentaries by Lecchi. Milan, 1752. 3 vols.
7. Arithmetica Universalis. Cambridge, 1707. First edition.
8. Arithmetica Universalis. Leyden edition. 1732.
9. Newton's Fluxions. French Translation, by Le Clerc. Paris, 1740.
10. Newton's Essay on Lines of the Third Order. Paris, 1797.

11. Newton's Principia. Amsterdam edition, 1714.

12. Newton's Principia. Cambridge edition, 1713. Brook Taylor's copy, with his inscription.

13. Translation or adaptation, of the Principia made by the Marquise du Chastelet. 2 vols., Paris, 1756.

14. Excerpta from the Principia. Cambridge, 1765. First edition.

15. Pemberton's Essay on the Principia. Italian Translation. Venice, 1733.

16. Lectures on the Principia. 2 vols., Naples, 1792, 1793.

17. Raphson's History of Fluxions, London, 1715. English edition. The Latin edition appeared in the same year.

18. Commercium Epistolicum. 1725 edition. This is Edition B of Gray's Bibliography, there having been two editions that year.

19. Newton's Optics. Lausanne and Geneva, 1740. This is the Third edition of the translation into Latin by Samuel Clarke, and is the copy specially bound and presented by the publishers to Jean Bernoulli.

20. A Collection of Monographs, the first of which is Raphson on the analysis of equations. London, 1690. Presentation copy by Raphson to Newton. With this is bound Cassini's Essay on the Comet of 1680. Paris, 1681. The essay contains a number of marginal notes in Newton's hand.

21. Historia Rerum Oriente Gestorum. Frankfort, 1587. Newton's copy, with his autograph.

22. Barrow's Lectures as Lucasian Professor in 1664. Newton attended these lectures as an undergraduate.

23. Catalogue of the Portsmouth papers written by Newton. Cambridge, 1888. Of the three editors, one was J. C. Adams, one of the discoverers of Neptune. This is a presentation copy from him and bears his autograph.

24. Address on the Life of Newton. Paolo Frisi, Milan, 1880. Presentation copy from Frisi's brother.

25. Loria's Biography of Newton. Rome, 1920. Presentation copy from the author.

26. Loria's work on the History of Science, containing an essay on Newton. Presentation copy from the author.

27. Euler's Letters to a German Princess, with a description of the Optics of Newton. Edited by Sir David Brewster. Autographed presentation copy from the editor.

28. Sir David Brewster's Life of Newton. London, 1831. From the bibliographical standpoint interesting as an unopened copy.

29. Sir David Brewster's Memoirs of Newton. Edinburgh, 1855.

30. Cajori's History of Fluxions, Chicago, 1919.

31. Hartill's Recollections of Newton House in Leicester Square. London, 1914.

32. Giramonti's Essay on the Life of Newton, without date (1827?)

33. Lord Brougham's Analytical View of the Principia. London, 1855. Presentation copy from Lord Brougham.

34. Jadelot's Méchanisme de la Nature, with an essay on Newton's Philosophy. London, 1787.

35. Maclaurin's Account of Newton's Philosophy. London, 1748.

36. Ball's Essay on Newton's Classification of Cubics. Cambridge, 1890.

37. Algarotti's Essay on the Philosophy of Newton. Glasgow, 1765.

38. Whewell's Essay on Newton's Principia. London, 1846.

39. Voltaire's Essay on the Newtonian Philosophy. Glasgow, 1764. English translation.

40. Voltaire's work on Élémens de la Philosohpie de Neuton. London, 1738. There was an Amsterdam edition the same year.
41. Giovanni del Turco. Address on Newton's Principia. Livorno, 1765.
42. De Morgan's Essay on Newton. London, 1914.
43. Bibliography of the works of Newton by Gray. Cambridge, 1907.
44. Manuscript of Jekuthiel Ginsburg's supplement to Gray's bibliography; upwards of 400 additional items.
45. 125 portraits of Newton.
46. 25 portrait medals or tokens of Newton.
47. Three documents (2 on vellum) signed by Newton, one bearing his seal.
48. Facsimiles of Newton manuscripts in the Pierpont Morgan library, as published in W. J. Greenstreet's compilation of articles on Newton, London, 1927.
49. A fragment of Newton's manuscript with geometric figure and computations.
50. In addition to the Newton material there were exhibited upwards of a hundred items relating to the immediate contemporaries of Newton in his fields of activity, and his most prominent predecessors and successors in these fields. They included autographs and autograph letters of Galileo, Wren, Ramus, Gassendi, Descartes, De Moivre, the Bernoullis and Cassinis, Picard, Voltaire, du Chastellet, and many others of similar standing.

IV. *Miscellaneous Items*

1. Two works presented by Newton to the library of Yale College soon after its foundation and now in the library of Yale University, namely Principia Mathe-

matica, Second edition, London, (1713); Optice, Latin edition, (1706).

2. A copy of Riccioli's Almagestum Novum, 1651. From Newton's library with annotations in his handwriting, and two pages of Newton's handwriting, lent by James Stokley, Esq. of Science Service.

Sans Tache

Sans Tache

IN THE "elder days of art" each artist or craftsman enjoyed the privilege of independent creation. He carried through a process of manufacture from beginning to end. The scribe of the days before the printing press was such a craftsman. So was the printer in the days before the machine process. He stood or fell, as a craftsman, by the merit or demerit of his finished product.

Modern machine production has added much to the worker's productivity and to his material welfare; but it has deprived him of the old creative distinctiveness. His work is merged in the work of the team, and lost sight of as something representing him and his personality.

Many hands and minds contribute to the manufacture of a book, in this day of specialization. There are seven distinct major processes in the making of a book: The type must first be set; by the monotype method, there are two processes, the "keyboarding" of the MS and the casting of the type from the perforated paper rolls thus produced. Formulas and other intricate work must be hand-set; then the whole brought together ("composed") in its true order, made into pages and forms. The results must be checked by proof reading at each stage. Then comes the "make-ready" and press-run and finally the binding into volumes.

All of these processes, except that of binding into cloth or leather covers, are carried on under our roof.

The motto of the Waverly Press is *Sans Tache*. Our ideal is to manufacture books *"without blemish"*—worthy books, worthily printed, with worthy typography—books to which we shall be proud to attach our imprint, made by craftsmen who are willing to accept open responsibility for their work, and who are entitled to credit for creditable performance.

The printing craftsman of today is quite as much a craftsman as his predecessor. There is quite as much discrimination between poor work and good. We are of the opinion that the individuality of the worker should not be wholly lost. The members of our staff who have contributed their skill of hand and brain to this volume are:

Keyboard: Vera Taylor, Mary Franck, Laurel Tourtellotte, Helen Twardowicz.

Caster: Kenneth Brown, Ernest Wann, Charles Aher, Martin Griffen, George Smith, Mahlon Robinson, Henry Lee, Charles Fick, George Bullinger.

Composing Room: Harry Susemihl, Harry Harmeyer, Herbert Leitch, Arthur Baker, James Jackson, Anthony Wagner, Andrew Rassa, Edward Rice, Richard King, George Moss, Theodore Nilson, Henry Shea.

Proof Room: Sarah Katzin, Mary Reed, Alice Reuter, Ruth Treishman, Ethel Strasinger, Dorothy Strasinger, Lucile Bull, Audrey Tanner, Angeline Eifert, Lilland Gilland, Ida Zinmerman.

Press: Wm. Harrison Jr., Emory Parsons, Andrew Becker, Robert Gallagher, Raymond Gallagher.

Folder: Lawrence Krug, Shipley Dellinger.

Cutter: William Armiger.

Date Due

DEC 2	NOV 11 1958	MAR 2	1970
	DEC 16 1959		
MAR 30		MAY 18	1980
APR 2	NOV 3 8 '60	MAY 18	1980
Ap 80	JAN 25 '61	MAY 09 1982	
	MR 13 '63	NOV 2 1982	
A	MY 8 '63		
F 22 '43	JY 24 '63	OCT 11 1985	
DEC 15	DE 18 '64	MAY 22 1986	
Mr 4 '53	FE 10 '65	MAY 19 1987	
DEC 12	DEC 15 1965		
NOV 1 1953	JAN 17 1966		
DEC 13	JAN 12 1967		
DEC 5 1956	9 1971		
DEC 11 1957			
MAR 26 1958	MAY 18 1972		
DEC 10 1958	NOV 16 1972		
FEB 4 1959			
MAR 8 1959			
NOV 1 1958			